MATHEMATICS

Statistics
Unit S3

Dr I G Evans

AS/A LEVEL

WJEC AS/A Level Mathematics
Statistics Unit S3

Published by the Welsh Joint Education Committee
245 Western Avenue, Cardiff, CF5 2YX

First published 2001

Printed by Hackman Printers Ltd
Clydach Vale, Tonypandy, Rhondda, CF40 2XX

ISBN: 1 86085 465 6

PREFACE

This book (the last in Statistics) covers the content of the specification for Unit S3 in the WJEC. A/AS Mathematics. The topics included are those that appeared in the Module S2 book but do not appear in the Unit S2 book.

As in the books covering Units S1 and S2, each chapter is sectionalised, with each section introducing a specific topic followed by worked examples and exercises. Each chapter ends with a collection of questions on the topics covered; the vast majority of these questions have been drawn from past examination papers (A3 and S2).

It should be noted that the tables used in the worked examples are *Elementary Statistical Tables* published originally by RND Publications but now being published by the WJEC. The solutions given will need to be modified if the tables being used are *Statistical Tables* by Murdoch and Barnes.

Notification to the author or the WJEC of any errors that may be found in this book would be appreciated.

CONTENTS

Chapter 1

Sampling Distributions

Introduction

A fundamental problem area in Statistics, known as **statistical inference**, is one in which the distribution of a random variable of interest is not known completely and a sample of observed values is to be used to make inferences about the distribution. The distribution which is to be sampled is often referred to as the **population distribution**. The two examples given below illustrate situations where inferences are appropriate.

Example 1. Estimating a population mean.

The manufacturer of a new low-energy light bulb wants an estimate of the mean operational lifetime of the bulbs. The estimate is to be made on the basis of the operational lifetimes of a sample of bulbs.

Let X hours denote the operational lifetime of such a bulb. In this case the distribution of X (for all such bulbs) is the population distribution, which is not known. The manufacturer wants an estimate of μ, the mean operational lifetime. Suppose that a sample of bulbs are tested and found to have a mean operational lifetime of $\bar{x}$ hours. Intuitively, it is sensible to take $\bar{x}$ as an estimate of μ, but how do we assess how likely it is to be close to μ?

Similar problems arise in many other areas of investigation, some examples of which are as follows :

(a) In education, a new approach to teaching Mathematics has been proposed and it is required to determine whether pupils taught by this approach will perform better, on average, than pupils taught by the traditional method. The new approach is to be used with a class of pupils who will then sit a standard test, the results of which are to be used to reach a conclusion about the new approach.

(b) In horticulture, a new fertiliser programme for growing tomatoes has been devised and is to be used on a sample of tomato plants. The mean yield of tomatoes from the sample of plants will be taken as an estimate of the mean yield for all plants grown under this programme.

(c) In medicine, a new treatment for a particular disease is applied to a sample of patients so as to estimate the mean time for the treatment to be effective.

Example 2. Estimating a probability or a proportion

A pharmaceutical company has developed a new drug for a particular disease and wishes to estimate its success rate θ, say. To estimate θ the drug is administered to a sample of patients and the sample success rate is used as an estimate of θ.

Other examples of this type include:

(a) Using a sample of voters to estimate the proportion of all voters in an electorate who will vote for a particular candidate in a forthcoming election.

(b) Sowing a sample of seeds of a new variety of flower and using the sample germination rate as the estimate of the overall germination rate of such seeds.

(c) Using a sample of mass-produced items to estimate the proportion of such items that are defective.

In each of the above examples a sample is used to estimate a population **parameter**, by which we mean some numerical characteristic of a probability distribution (the population mean in Example 1 and the population proportion in Example 2).

Definition. Any quantity which is calculated from a sample of values for the purpose of estimating a population parameter is called a **statistic**.

In Example 1 above the statistic used was the sample mean, while in Example 2 the statistic was the sample proportion of 'successes'. But how good were these choices? What sort of discrepancy can we expect between the sample estimate and the true value of the parameter? To answer these questions we need to take account of the fact that different samples will generally lead to different estimates.

Let T denote a description of how the sample values are to be combined to give an estimate of the parameter of interest. T is itself a random variable, the distribution of which can be obtained by generating all possible samples of the given size, each of which will give a value t of T. Because the distribution of a statistic is deduced from all possible samples it is aptly referred to as its **sampling distribution**.

To enable us to determine a sampling distribution it is necessary to impose some conditions on the method of sampling. The essential condition is that the method used should be such that every possible sample of the given size has the same chance of being selected.

Before developing some theoretical results concerning the sampling distributions of certain statistics it is instructive to derive some sampling distributions in simple situations. In the next section we consider a simple example of sampling without replacement from a finite collection of objects each of which has a numerical value, and in the subsequent section we look at a situation where the sample consists of independent observations of a random variable.

1.1 Sampling without replacement from a finite population

Consider a population (collection) of N objects and let X be a random variable which assigns a numerical value to each object in the population. In the case when the X-values of the objects are not known the objective may be to take a random sample of n of the objects without replacement and to use their X-values to estimate some parameter (e.g. the mean) of the distribution of X. The following example illustrates how to find the sampling distributions of some statistics when sampling without replacement from a finite population.

Example

A pack of ten cards consists of five cards bearing the number 1, three bearing the number 2, and the two remaining cards bearing the number 3.

(a) Find the mean μ, and the median, γ, of the numbers on the cards in the pack.

Three of the cards are drawn at random without replacement.

(b) Find the sampling distribution of the mean $\overline{X}$ of the three numbers on the chosen cards. Hence find the mean of the sampling distribution and compare its value with that of the population mean.

(c) Find the sampling distribution of the median M of the three numbers on the chosen cards. Hence find the mean of the sampling distribution and compare its value with the population median.

(d) Find the sampling distribution of the proportion Y of the numbers on the chosen cards that equal 1. Hence find the mean of the sampling distribution and compare its value with the population proportion of cards that are numbered 1.

Solution

(a) In order of magnitude the numbers on the ten cards are
$$1, 1, 1, 1, 1, 2, 2, 2, 3, 3.$$
The mean of these numbers is $\mu = 17/10 = 1.7$.

The median is the middle value or, since here there are ten numbers, it is the average of the fifth and sixth numbers when ordered from smallest to largest. Hence, the median is
$$\gamma = \tfrac{1}{2}(1 + 2) = 1.5.$$
If we let X denote the number on a randomly chosen card then the distribution of X is as follows :

x	1	2	3
P(X = x)	0.5	0.3	0.2

The mean of this distribution is $\mu = 1.7$ and its median is $\gamma = 1.5$.

To derive a sampling distribution we first need to generate all the possible samples of size three from the population of ten cards and determine their probabilities. We can then obtain the value of any statistic for each sample and deduce the sampling distribution of that statistic. In the situation considered here it is much easier to deal with unordered samples than ordered samples as there are fewer of them and any collection of three numbers in whatever order they occur will give the same value for a statistic. Now, the total number of possible unordered samples of size 3 drawn without replacement from a population of size 10 is $\binom{10}{3} = 120$. One possible unordered sample of values is $\{1,1,3\}$.

Since this consists of two 1's (chosen from 5) and one 3 (chosen from 2) the number of ways that this unordered sample could arise is $\binom{5}{3} \times \binom{2}{1} = 20$, so that the probability of this unordered sample is 20/120.

Similarly, the unordered sample $\{1, 2, 3\}$ has probability $\binom{5}{1} \times \binom{3}{1} \times \binom{2}{1} / 120 = 30/120$.

All the possible unordered samples are listed in the first column of the following table. The second column lists the probabilities of these samples, while the remaining columns show the corresponding values of the three statistics $\overline{X}$, M and Y.

Sample	Probability		$\overline{X}$	M	Y
(1, 1, 1)	$\binom{5}{3}/120$	$= 10/120$	1	1	1
(1, 1, 2)	$\binom{5}{2} \times \binom{3}{1}/120$	$= 30/120$	$1\frac{1}{3}$	1	$\frac{2}{3}$
(1, 1, 3)	$\binom{5}{2} \times \binom{2}{1}/120$	$= 20/120$	$1\frac{2}{3}$	1	$\frac{2}{3}$
(1, 2, 2)	$\binom{5}{1} \times \binom{3}{2}/120$	$= 15/120$	$1\frac{2}{3}$	2	$\frac{1}{3}$
(1, 2, 3)	$\binom{5}{1} \times \binom{3}{1} \times \binom{2}{1}/120$	$= 30/120$	2	2	$\frac{1}{3}$
(1, 3, 3)	$\binom{5}{1} \times \binom{2}{2}/120$	$= 5/120$	$2\frac{1}{3}$	3	$\frac{1}{3}$
(2, 2, 2)	$\binom{3}{3}/120$	$= 1/120$	2	2	0
(2, 2, 3)	$\binom{3}{2} \times \binom{2}{1}/120$	$= 6/120$	$2\frac{1}{3}$	2	0
(2, 3, 3)	$\binom{3}{1} \times \binom{2}{2}/120$	$= 3/120$	$2\frac{2}{3}$	3	0

[The probabilities do add to unity as they should - an advisable check!]

(b) From the above table we find that the sampling distribution of $\overline{X}$ is as given in the following table.

$\overline{x}$	1	$1\frac{1}{3}$	$1\frac{2}{3}$	2	$2\frac{1}{3}$	$2\frac{2}{3}$
$P(\overline{X} = \overline{x})$	$\dfrac{10}{120}$	$\dfrac{30}{120}$	$\dfrac{35}{120}$	$\dfrac{31}{120}$	$\dfrac{11}{120}$	$\dfrac{3}{120}$

The mean of this sampling distribution is

$$E(\overline{X}) = \frac{1}{120}\left(1 \times 10 + \frac{4}{3} \times 30 + \frac{5}{3} \times 35 + 2 \times 31 + \frac{7}{3} \times 11 + \frac{8}{3} \times 3\right) = \frac{612}{360} = 1.7 = \mu.$$

Thus, the average value of $\overline{x}$ over all possible samples is equal to μ. Its most probable value is seen to be $1\frac{2}{3}$.

(c)   Referring back to our table of outcomes and their probabilities the sampling distribution of the sample median M is :

m	1	2	3
P(M = m)	$\dfrac{60}{120}$	$\dfrac{52}{120}$	$\dfrac{8}{120}$

It follows that the mean value of M over all possible samples is

$$E(M) = \frac{1}{120}(1 \times 60 + 2 \times 52 + 3 \times 8) = \frac{188}{120} = 1\frac{17}{30} \cong 1.57$$

which is close to but not equal to the population median $\gamma = 1.5$. Also, the most probable value of M is 1.

(d)   Again referring back to our table of outcomes and probabilities we find that the sampling distribution of Y is as follows.

y	0	$\dfrac{1}{3}$	$\dfrac{2}{3}$	1
P(Y = y)	$\dfrac{10}{120}$	$\dfrac{50}{120}$	$\dfrac{50}{120}$	$\dfrac{10}{120}$

The mean value of Y over all possible samples is

$$E(Y) = \frac{1}{120}(0 \times 10 + \frac{1}{3} \times 50 + \frac{2}{3} \times 50 + 1 \times 10) = \frac{60}{120} = \frac{1}{2},$$

which is equal to $P(X = 1)$, the proportion of 1's in the population. Also, there is no unique most probable value of Y, the values 1/3 and 2/3 being equally most probable. Summarising the above we see that both the sample mean and the sample proportion of 1's have mean values that are equal to the population mean and proportion of 1's, respectively, results which are **always true** when sampling without replacement from a finite population.

Exercise 1.1

1. With reference to the pack of 10 cards in the above example, find the sampling distributions of $\overline{X}_2$ and $\overline{X}_4$, where $\overline{X}_r$ (r = 2, 4) is the mean of the numbers on r cards chosen at random without replacement from the pack.   Verify that each sampling distribution has mean equal to μ (the population mean). Also calculate the variances of the sampling distributions and comment on their relative values.

2. A money box contains six coins, one each of 5p and 20p coins, and two each of 10p and 50p coins. Two coins are chosen at random without replacement. Find the sampling distribution of their total value and the probability that their total value exceeds 30p.

3. Five cards numbered 1, 2, 3, 4 and 5 are placed in a box. Three of the cards are chosen at random without replacement. Find the sampling distribution of

(a) the median of the three chosen numbers,

(b) the smallest of the three chosen numbers.

4. A subcommittee of three people is to be formed from a committee of six people. Of the six people on the committee, two are 30 years old, one is 32, two are 33 and one is 37. Obtain the sampling distributions of the mean and median age of the subcommittee if it is selected at random.

5. A bag contains 3 red balls and 2 blue balls. Two balls are chosen at random without replacement from the bag. Let Y denote the proportion of red balls in the sample. Find the sampling distribution of Y and verify that its expected value is equal to the proportion of red balls in the bag.

6. The number of days that each of 5 employees (A, B, C, D, E) in an office was absent from work during a year is shown in the following table.

Employee	A	B	C	D	E
Number of days absent	10	6	0	4	0

(a) Calculate the mean μ and the variance σ^2 of the numbers of days these employees were absent from work.

(b) Three of the employees are chosen at random without replacement. Let $\overline{X}$ denote the mean number of days absent for the three chosen employees. Determine the sampling distribution of $\overline{X}$ and verify that $E(\overline{X}) = \mu$ and $Var(\overline{X}) = \sigma^2/6$.

7. A carton contains 10 boxes of matches, 3 of which contain 46 matches, 6 contain 47 matches, and the remaining one contains 48 matches. Calculate the mean number μ of matches per box in the carton. A sample of three boxes is drawn without replacement from the carton. Let $\overline{X}$ denote the mean number of matches per box sampled. Find the sampling distribution of $\overline{X}$. Verify that $E(\overline{X}) = \mu$ and evaluate $Var(\overline{X})$.

8. The five flats in a block are occupied by families A, B, C, D and E. Each of families A and B has no child, each of families C and D has one child, and family E has two children. Find (a) the mean number of children per family, (b) the proportion of the families that have no child.

(c) Three of the families are chosen at random without replacement. Find the sampling distribution of (i) the mean number of children in the sample, (ii) the proportion of families in the sample having no child. Verify that the means of these sampling distributions are equal to the corresponding population values.

1.2 Sampling from a distribution

Let X denote a random variable defined with respect to a particular random experiment which can be repeated indefinitely under identical conditions. For example, X could be the score obtained when a die is thrown or some numerical quality characteristic of a mass-produced item. Let $X_1, X_2, \ldots, X_n$ denote the outcomes of n independent trials of the random experiment. Then $X_1, X_2, \ldots, X_n$ are independent random variables (since the trials are independent) and each has the same distribution as X. We refer to $X_1, X_2, \ldots, X_n$ as being a **random sample of n observations of X**. Sampling with replacement from a finite population is a special case where the above conditions are satisfied. However, this is not so when the sampling from a finite population is without replacement since the conditions vary from one trial to the next, the population size decreasing by one after each trial.

Throughout the remainder of this text we shall be assuming that any sample is a random sample of observations of a random variable as defined above. The following example derives the sampling distributions of some statistics based on a random sample of three observations of a simple discrete random variable.

Example

A circular spinner is divided into ten equal sectors, six of which are numbered 1, three are numbered 2 and the remaining sector is numbered 3. In any spin the pointer on the spinner is equally likely to stop in any one of the sectors and the score obtained is the number on that sector. Let X denote the score in any one spin. Then, the distribution of X (the population distribution) is as follows.

x	1	2	3
P(X =x)	0.6	0.3	0.1

The mean of this distribution is $\mu \equiv E(X) = 1 \times 0.6 + 2 \times 0.3 + 3 \times 0.1 = 1.5$.

Consider three spins. Denote the scores that will be obtained by X_1, X_2, X_3, respectively. Observe that X_1, X_2, X_3 are independent random variables each having the same distribution as X. Let us now find the sampling distributions of

(a) $\overline{X}$, the mean of three scores, (b) Y, the proportion of the three scores that equal 1.

Solution

We first need to consider all the possible samples of 3 observations of X. Since each spin can give any one of three possible scores the total number of **ordered** outcomes in three spins is $3 \times 3 \times 3 = 27$. As in Section 1.1 it is easier to consider all possible **unordered** outcomes. One possible unordered outcome is {1, 2, 2}. Since the 1 could occur in any of the three spins there are three ordered outcomes giving the unordered outcome {1, 2, 2}. Similarly, the unordered outcome {1, 2, 3} can result from any one of 6 possible ordered outcomes. The following table lists all the possible unordered outcomes, the associated numbers of ordered outcomes, the probabilities of the unordered outcomes and the values of $\overline{X}$ and Y.

Unordered outcome	Number of ordered outcomes	Probability		$\overline{X}$	Y
{1, 1, 1}	1	$(0.6)^3$	$= 0.216$	1	1
{1, 1, 2}	3	$3(0.6)^2(0.3)$	$= 0.324$	$1\frac{1}{3}$	$\frac{2}{3}$
{1, 1, 3}	3	$3(0.6)^2(0.1)$	$= 0.108$	$1\frac{2}{3}$	$\frac{2}{3}$
{1, 2, 2)}	3	$3(0.6)(0.3)^2$	$= 0.162$	$1\frac{2}{3}$	$\frac{1}{3}$
{1, 2, 3}	6	$6(0.6)(0.3)(0.1)$	$= 0.108$	2	$\frac{1}{3}$
{1, 3, 3}	3	$3(0.6)(0.1)^2$	$= 0.018$	$2\frac{1}{3}$	$\frac{1}{3}$
{2, 2, 2}	1	$(0.3)^3$	$= 0.027$	2	0
{2, 2, 3}	3	$3(0.3)^2(0.1)$	$= 0.027$	$2\frac{1}{3}$	0
{2, 3, 3}	3	$3(0.3)(0.1)^2$	$= 0.009$	$2\frac{2}{3}$	0
{3, 3, 3}	1	$(0.1)^3$	$= 0.001$	3	0
Totals	27		1.000		

[The two totals are shown to provide checks.]

(a) From the third and fourth columns of the table we find that the sampling distribution of $\overline{X}$ is as follows :

$\overline{x}$	1	$1\frac{1}{3}$	$1\frac{2}{3}$	2	$2\frac{1}{3}$	$2\frac{2}{3}$	3
$P(\overline{X} = \overline{x})$	0.216	0.324	0.270	0.135	0.045	0.009	0.001

The mean of this sampling distribution is

$$E(\overline{X}) = 1\times0.216 + \frac{4}{3}\times0.324 + \frac{5}{3}\times0.270 + 2\times0.135 + \frac{7}{3}\times0.045 + \frac{8}{3}\times0.009 + 3\times0.001$$

$$= 1.5$$

which is equal to $E(X)$, the population mean, but note that no observed sample mean will be equal to the population mean.

(b) From the third and fifth columns of the table of outcomes the sampling distribution of Y = proportion of 1's in the sample is as follows.

Y	0	$\frac{1}{3}$	$\frac{2}{3}$	1
$P(Y = y)$	0.064	0.288	0.432	0.216

It follows that

$$E(Y) = 0 \times 0.064 + \frac{1}{3} \times 0.288 + \frac{2}{3} \times 0.432 + 1 \times 0.216 = 0.6,$$

which is equal to $P(X = 1)$.

[In Chapter 2 we will show that the mean of a random sample of observations of a random variable always has an expected value equal to the population mean and that a sample proportion always has an expected value equal to the corresponding population proportion.]

Exercise 1.2

1. A random experiment has the three possible outcomes 0, 1 and 2 which occur with probabilities 0.2, 0.6 and 0.2, respectively. Let X denote the outcome of one trial and let $\overline{X}$ denote the mean of the outcomes of three independent trials of the random experiment. Find the sampling distribution of $\overline{X}$ and verify that

(a) $E(\overline{X}) = E(X)$ and (b) $Var(\overline{X}) = \frac{1}{3}Var(X)$.

2. With reference to the worked example above find the sampling distribution of the sample median M. Evaluate $E(M)$.

3. Let X_1 and X_2 denote the first and second of two independent observations of the random variable X whose distribution is given in the following table.

x	0	1	2
$P(X = x)$	0.3	0.4	0.3

(a) List all the possible ordered outcomes (X_1, X_2) and evaluate their probabilities.
(b) Find the sampling distribution of $\overline{X}$, the mean of X_1 and X_2. Verify that $E(\overline{X}) = E(X)$ and $Var(\overline{X}) = \dfrac{1}{2} Var(X)$.

(c) Find the sampling distribution of $W = \dfrac{1}{2}(X_1 - X_2)^2$. Verify that $E(W) = Var(X)$.

4. A fair cubical die has three of its faces numbered 1, two other faces numbered 2 and the remaining face numbered 3. When the die is thrown the score X is defined to be the number showing on the uppermost face Write down the distribution of X and evaluate its mean and variance.

(a) Let $\overline{X}$ denote the mean of the scores in three throws of the die. Derive the sampling distribution of $\overline{X}$. Evaluate $E(\overline{X})$ and $Var(\overline{X})$ and compare their values with $E(X)$ and $Var(X)$, respectively.

(b) Let M denote the median of the three scores. Find the sampling distribution of M and evaluate $E(M)$.

(c) Let R denote the range of the three scores (that is, the highest minus the lowest). Find the sampling distribution of R and evaluate $E(R)$.

(d) Let P denote the proportion of 1's obtained in three throws. Find the sampling distribution of P and verify that $E(P) = P(X = 1)$.

5. X_1 and X_2 are two independent observations of the random variable X where
$$P(X = x) = \frac{1}{3}, \quad \text{for } x = 1, 2, 3.$$
Derive the sampling distribution of $Y = X_1/X_2$ and show that $E(Y) \neq E(X_1)/E(X_2)$.

1.3 Sampling distribution of a sample mean

1.3.1 A general result

Recall from Section 2.5 of the S2 book that if $\overline{X}$ is the mean of a random sample of n observations of the random variable X whose mean is μ and whose variance is σ^2 then the sampling distribution of $\overline{X}$ is such that

$$E(\overline{X}) = \mu \quad \text{and} \quad \text{Var}(\overline{X}) = \sigma^2/n$$

Example

Let $\overline{X}$ denote the mean of a random sample of 27 observations of the continuous random variable X which is uniformly distributed over the interval from 1 to 10. Find the mean and the standard deviation of $\overline{X}$.

Solution

Since $X \sim U[1,10]$ we have

$$E(X) = (1 + 10)/2 = 5.5 \quad \text{and} \quad \text{Var}(X) = (10 - 1)^2/12 = 6.75$$

Hence, using the results given above

$$E(\overline{X}) = E(X) = 5.5 \quad \text{and Var}(\overline{X}) = 6.75/27 = 0.25$$

Hence $\overline{X}$ has mean 5.5 and standard deviation $\sqrt{0.25} = 0.5$

Exercise 1.3a

1. The random variable X has the distribution shown in the following table.

x	0	1	2
P(X = x)	0.4	0.4	0.2

Find the mean and the variance of $\overline{X}$, where $\overline{X}$ is the mean of a random sample of 14 observations of X.

2. A balanced tetrahedral die has its faces numbered 1, 2, 3, 4 respectively. When this die is thrown onto a table the score obtained is the number on the face in contact with the table. It may be assumed that the score obtained on any throw is equally likely to be 1, 2, 3, 4. The die is thrown 12 times.

Determine the mean and the variance of the mean of the 14 scores.

3. The continuous random variable X has probability density function f given by

$$f(x) = x + 0.5, \quad \text{for } 0 \leq x \leq 1.$$

Find the mean and the variance of the mean of a random sample 11 observations of X.

4. The continuous random variable X has probability density function f, where

$$f(x) = 3(100 - x)^2/10^6, \quad \text{for } 0 < x < 100.$$

Determine the mean and the variance of X. Hence determine the mean and the variance of the mean of a random sample of 4 observations of X.

5. Find the mean and the standard deviation of the mean of a random sample of 10 observations of the random variable which has the Poisson distribution with mean 2.5.

6. Let $\overline{X}$ denote the mean of a random sample of n observations of a random variable whose standard deviation is 4. Find the smallest value of n if the standard deviation of $\overline{X}$ is to be at most 0.5.

1.3.2 The Central Limit Theorem

The Central Theorem states that if $\overline{X}$ is the mean of a random sample of observations of the random variable X whose mean is μ and whose standard deviation is σ then, for large n, the sampling distribution of $\overline{X}$ is approximately normal. That is,

$$\overline{X} \approx N(\mu, \sigma^2/n) \tag{1}$$

Establishing this result requires mathematics beyond the level of this text.

Recall from Section 2.5 of the S2 book that (1) is exactly true if X is normally dsitributed. How large n must be for the approximation in (1) to be reasonably good depends on the shape of the distribution of X. Generally, the more symmetrical the distribution of X the smaller n need be for (1) to be a good approximation.

[Computer simulations of observations from a specified distribution, e.g U(0,1) , can be used to demonstrate the Central Limit Theorem by taking several samples of size n (for different values of n) and drawing the histograms of the sample means obtained].

Denoting the sample observations by $X_1, X_2, \ldots, X_n$, note that (1) is equivalent to

$$\sum_{i=1}^{n} X_i \approx N(n\mu, n\sigma^2) \tag{2}$$

and

$$\frac{\overline{X} - \mu}{\sigma / \sqrt{n}} \approx N(0, 1) \tag{3}$$

If X is a discrete random variable then so is $\overline{X}$ discrete. Since (1) requires approximating a discrete distribution by a continuous normal distribution, better approximations to probabilities about $\overline{X}$ may be obtained by applying the appropriate correction for continuity, as we did when using normal approximations to the binomial and Poisson distributions in Section 1.7 of the S2 book. In the case of a discrete X whose possible values are consecutive integers the consecutive values of $\overline{X}$ will differ by 1/n so that the appropriate continuity correction factor is 1/(2n). However, the possible values of S = the sum of the observations will also be consecutive integers so that for S the continuity correction will be 0.5 as in Section 1.7 of the S2 book. Thus, there is some advantage in using (2) rather than (1) when X is a discrete random variable restricted to consecutive integer values. This is illustrated in the following example.

Example 1

Find an approximate value for the probability that the mean score obtained in 30 throws of a fair cubical die will be 4 or more.

Solution

Let X denote the score in one throw of the die. Since the die is fair

$$P(X = x) = \frac{1}{6}, \quad \text{for } x = 1, 2, 3, 4, 5, 6.$$

By symmetry, or otherwise, the mean of this distribution is $\mu = E(X) = 3\frac{1}{2}$ and its variance is

$$\sigma^2 = \text{Var}(X) = E(X^2) - \mu^2 = \frac{1}{6}(1 + 4 + 9 + 16 + 25 + 36) - \left(\frac{7}{2}\right)^2 = \frac{35}{12}.$$

Since X is discrete we shall use (2) to answer the question posed. Let $X_1, X_2, \ldots, X_{30}$ denote the scores obtained in the 30 throws. Using (2) the distribution of S = the sum of the 30 scores is approximately normal with

$$\text{mean} = 30 \times 3.5 = 105 \text{ and variance} = 30 \times (35/12) = 1050/12.$$

We want an approximate value of $P(\overline{X} \geq 4)$, where $\overline{X} = S/30$ is the mean of the scores.

$$P(\overline{X} \geq 4) \equiv P(S \geq 120) \equiv P(S > 119.5), \text{ on applying the correction for continuity}$$

$$\cong P\left(Z > \frac{119.5 - 105}{\sqrt{1050/12}}\right) \cong P(Z > 1.55) \cong 0.061.$$

[Using (1) the sample mean $\overline{X}$ is approximately normally distributed with

$$\text{mean} = 3.5 \text{ and variance} = \frac{35}{360}.$$

Ignoring the continuity correction (which in this case is 1/60) we have

$$P(\overline{X} \geq 4) = P\left(Z \geq \frac{4 - 3.5}{\sqrt{35/360}}\right) \cong P(Z \geq 1.60) \cong 0.055.$$

Applying the continuity correction (1/60) here would lead to the answer 0.061 given above.]

Example 2

The continuous random variable X is distributed with mean 25.8 and standard deviation 2.4. Use a distributional approximation to evaluate the probability that the mean of a random sample of 50 observations of X will be less than 26.

Solution

Let $\overline{X}$ denote the sample mean. Using (1) we know that
$$\overline{X} \approx N(25.8, 2.4^2/50).$$
Using this approximation,

$$P(\overline{X} < 26) \cong P\left(Z < \frac{26 - 25.8}{2.4/\sqrt{50}} \right) \cong P(Z < 0.59) \cong 0.722$$

[Note that a continuity correction was not necessary here because X is a continuous random variable.]

Exercise 1.3b

1. Find an approximate value for the probability that the mean of the scores in 50 throws of a fair cubical die will be between 3 and 4, both inclusive.

2. The discrete random variable X has the distribution shown in the following table.

x	1	2	3
P(X = x)	0.6	0.3	0.1

Find an approximate value for the probability that the mean of a random sample of 80 observations of X will be greater than 1.65.

3. Analysis of novels written by a certain author showed that the mean and the standard deviation of the number of words per sentence were 24 and 5, respectively. Find an approximate value for the probability that the mean number of words per sentence in a random sample of 100 sentences will be at least 25.

4. The masses of bags of peat are distributed with mean 25.1 kg and standard deviation 0.4 kg. Find an approximate value for the probability that a random sample of 50 bags will have

(a) a mean mass less than 25 kg, (b) a total mass exceeding 1260 kg.

5. The times that patients spend in a doctor's consulting room are distributed with mean 5 minutes and standard deviation 2 minutes. The doctor is to see 30 patients during a morning surgery which starts at 9.00 a.m. Find an approximate value for the probability that the doctor will have seen all 30 patients before 12.00 p.m.

6. Let $\overline{X}$ denote the mean of a random sample of 50 observations of the random variable X whose probability density function f is given by

$$f(x) = 2x, \qquad \text{for } 0 \le x \le 1.$$

Find an approximate value for $P(\overline{X} > 0.6)$

7. Let $\overline{X}$ denote the mean of a random sample of 80 observations of X, where X has probability density function f given by

$$f(x) = \frac{3}{4} x(2 - x), \qquad \text{for } 0 < x < 2.$$

Find approximate values for (a) $P(\overline{X} < 1)$, (b) $P(\overline{X} > 0.95)$.

8. The continuous random variable X has probability density function f, where

$$f(x) = \frac{1}{2}, \qquad \text{for } 0 \le x \le 1,$$

$$f(x) = \frac{1}{4}(3 - x), \qquad \text{for } 1 < x \le 3.$$

Find an approximate value for the probability that the mean of a random sample of 100 observations of X will be less than 1.

9. The thickness of books acquired by a library is a random variable with mean 3 cm and standard deviation 1 cm. The librarian orders 1000 books, for which 30.2 m of shelving is available. Find, approximately, the probability that these books can be accommodated by this shelving. Find also how much extra shelving would be required to ensure that the 1000 books can be accommodated with probability 0.95.

10. When a number is rounded to its nearest integer value the rounding error is defined to be the actual number minus its rounded value. When numbers are rounded to their nearest integer values the rounding errors may be regarded as independent observations from a uniform distribution over the interval $(- 0.5, + 0.5)$. Given that 75 numbers are rounded to their nearest integer values, find an approximate value for the probability that the mean rounding error will be **numerically** less than 0.05.

1.4 Sampling distribution of a proportion

Let X denote the number of successes in n independent Bernoulli trials in each of which the probability of a success is θ, where the value of θ is not known. We know that X has the distribution $B(n, \theta)$ and that $E(X) = n\theta$ and $Var(X) = n\theta(1 - \theta)$. The sample proportion of successes is $P = X/n$, which is an intuitively sensible statistic for estimating θ. The sampling distribution of P is such that

$$E(P) = \frac{1}{n}E(X) = \theta \quad \text{and} \quad Var(P) = \frac{1}{n^2}Var(X) = \frac{\theta(1-\theta)}{n}.$$

The above properties of a sample proportion are valid more generally than may at first appear. For instance, let X denote a quality measurement of a mass-produced item and suppose that an item is satisfactory only if X exceeds some specified value c. Then the proportion of the items produced that are satisfactory is $\theta = P(X > c)$. If P denotes the proportion of satisfactory items in a random sample of n items then the sampling distribution of P will have mean and variance as given above. As another example where the above results apply, let θ be the proportion of objects in a collection of objects which have a particular attribute (e.g. θ may be the proportion of all the pupils in a school who have a pet dog). Then, if a random sample of n objects is drawn **with replacement** from the collection, the sample proportion P having the attribute has mean and variance as given above. If a random sample of n objects is drawn **without replacement** from a collection of objects then the sample proportion P will be such that the above results are **approximately** true provided n is very small relative to the number N of objects in the collection. (This follows because when n/N is small the probability that an object drawn at random from the collection will remain roughly constant throughout the sampling.)

To verify the results given above consider the example in Section 1.2, where the distribution of X was as follows.

x	1	2	3
P(X = x)	0.6	0.3	0.1

In a random sample of 3 observations of X, we let Y denote the sample proportion of 1's and showed that the sampling distribution of Y was as follows

y	0	$\frac{1}{3}$	$\frac{2}{3}$	1
P(Y = y)	0.064	0.288	0.432	0.216

In Section 1.2 we showed that $E(Y) = 0.6 = P(X = 1)$, agreeing with the general result given above.

$$E(Y)^2 = \frac{1}{9} \times 0.288 + \frac{4}{9} \times 0.432 + 1 \times 0.216 = 0.44$$

Hence, $\quad Var(Y) = 0.44 - 0.6^2 = 0.08$.

Since $n = 3$ and $\theta = P(X = 1) = 0.6$ the result given above (with Y for P), gives

$$Var(Y) = 0.6 \times 0.4/3 = 0.08,$$

agreeing with the value we obtained from the sampling distribution of Y.

Example

In a random sample of 50 observations of the random variable X which is normally distributed with mean 20 and standard deviation 2, find the mean and the variance of the sample proportion of values that are greater than 22.

Solution

Here, $\theta = P(X > 22) = P\left(Z > \dfrac{22 - 20}{2}\right) = P(Z > 1) = 0.1586$.

Since n = 50 the mean and the variance of the sampling proportion, P, of values that are greater than 22 are :

$$E(P) = \theta = 0.1586 \text{ and } Var(P) = 0.1586 \times 0.8414/50 = 0.0027,\text{ correct to}$$

four decimal places.

Exercise 1.4

1. Four balls are drawn at random **with replacement** from a bag containing 7 red balls and 3 white balls. Let P denote the proportion of the drawn balls that are red. Derive the sampling distribution of P and verify the results given in this section for E(P) and Var(P).

2. A factory produces a very large number of items each day. The probability that an item selected at random will be found to be defective is 0.04. A random sample of 100 items is taken from the items produced during a particular day. Calculate the variance of the proportion of defectives in the sample.

3. A fair cubical die has three of its faces numbered 1, two faces numbered 2 and the remaining face numbered 3. The die is thrown 20 times. Let P_1 denote the proportion of times that a score of 1 is obtained, P_2 the proportion of times that a score of 2 is obtained, and P_3 the proportion of times that a score of 3 is obtained. Calculate the mean and the variance of (a) P_1, (b) P_2, (c) P_3.

4. The mass, X g, of inedibles per kg of a particular joint of meat is distributed with probability density function f given by

$$f(x) = \frac{3}{10^6}(100 - x)^2, \qquad \text{for } 0 < x < 100.$$

A joint of mass 1 kg is regarded as substandard if its inedible content exceeds 75 g. Calculate the probability that such a joint will be regarded as substandard. Given a random sample of 10 joints of mass 1 kg find the mean and the variance of the proportion of the joints in the sample that will be regarded as substandard.

5. The random variable X has probability density function f, where

$$f(x) = \frac{1}{4}(2 + x), \qquad \text{for} -1 < x < 1.$$

Given a random sample of 15 observations of X find the mean and the variance of the proportion of the sample observations that are positive.

Miscellaneous Questions on Chapter 1

1. (1987) The discrete random variable X has the distribution

$$P(X = 1) = 0.4, \quad P(X = 2) = 0.2, \quad P(X = 3) = 0.4$$

Calculate the variance of X. Let X_1 and X_2 denote two independent observations of X. Derive the sampling distribution of $T = \frac{1}{2}(X_1 - X_2)^2$ and verify that $E(T) = Var(X)$.   (7)

2. (1988) Four cards are numbered 2, 2, 4 and 6, respectively. Two of these cards are chosen at random without replacement. Let Y denote the larger of the numbers on the chosen cards. (Take Y = 2 if both cards are numbered 2). Determine the sampling distribution of Y and hence find the expected value of the larger of the two numbers.   (5)

3. (1989) Let $\overline{X}$ denote the mean of a random sample of 15 observations of the random variable X which is distributed with probability density function f, where

$$f(x) = \frac{3x^2}{\alpha^3}, \qquad \text{for } 0 \leq x \leq \alpha.$$

Calculate the mean and the variance of $\overline{X}$ in terms of α.   (5)

4. (1991) A small housing estate consists of ten bungalows. Three of the bungalows have 2 bedrooms, six have 3 bedrooms, and the remaining one has 4 bedrooms.
(a) Calculate the mean, μ, and the standard deviation, σ, of the number of bedrooms per bungalow on the estate.   (3)
(b)   A sample of three of the ten bungalows is to be chosen at random (**without replacement**).   Let $\overline{X}$ denote the mean number of bedrooms in the three chosen bungalows.
(i) There are seven possible combinations of the numbers of bedrooms in the three chosen bungalows. The following table shows three of these combinations together with their probabilities and the corresponding values of $\overline{X}$. Copy this table and insert the remaining

possible combinations together with their probabilities and the corresponding values of
$\overline{X}$.   (6)

Combinations	Probability	$\overline{X}$
(2, 2, 2)	$\dfrac{1}{120}$	2
(2, 2, 3)	$\dfrac{18}{120}$	$2\dfrac{1}{3}$
(2, 2, 4)	$\dfrac{3}{120}$	$2\dfrac{2}{3}$

(ii) Verify that $E(\overline{X}) = \mu$ and evaluate $Var(\overline{X})$.

(c) Suppose, instead that the bungalows are to be sampled at random **with replacement**. Find the smallest sample size that will have to be taken for the variance of the sample mean number of bedrooms per bungalow in this case to be less than the variance of $\overline{X}$.

(3)

5. (1992) An envelope contains 10 stamps, including 7 of value 20 pence and 3 of value 25 pence.

(i) Find the mean, μ, and the variance, σ^2, of the values of these 10 stamps.   (3)

Four of the 10 stamps are chosen at random. Let T_1 denote the total value of the 4 chosen stamps if they are chosen **without replacement**, and let T_2 denote their total value if they are chosen **with replacement**.

(ii) Find the sampling distribution of T_1 and evaluate its mean and variance. Explain why $E(T_1) = 4\mu$ and why $Var(T_1) \neq 4\sigma^2$.   (6)

(iii) Find the sampling distribution of T_2 and evaluate its mean and variance. Explain how the values of $E(T_2)$ and $Var(T_2)$ could have been obtained without first finding the sampling distribution of T_2.   (6)

6. (1994) A random sample of 50 observations is taken from a continuous distribution with mean 4 and standard deviation 2. Calculate an approximation to the probability that the mean of the 50 observations exceeds 4.3. Give your answer correct to 2 decimal places.   (4)

7. (1995) A bag contains six cards; two of the cards are numbered 1, two are numbered 2 and two are numbered 3. Three cards are selected at random from the bag without replacement.

(a) Construct a table showing all possible combinations of numbers on the three selected cards together with their probabilities.

(b) Deduce the probability distribution of the median of these three numbers.   (7)

8. (S2 1996) The discrete random variable X takes the values 1, 2, 3 with probabilities $\frac{1}{6}$, $\frac{1}{3}$, $\frac{1}{2}$, respectively. A random sample of two observations, X_1 and X_2, is taken from the distribution of X. Enumerate all possible pairs of values for X_1 and X_2. Hence find the sampling distributions of (a) the sum $S = X_1 + X_2$, (b) the range $R = |X_1 - X_2|$.   (6)

9. (A3 1996) The distribution of the daily amount of petrol, X thousand litres, sold by a service station, is modelled by the probability density function f given by
$$f(x) = kx^2(4 - x), \quad \text{for } 0 \le x \le 4.$$
(a) Show that $k = \dfrac{3}{64}$.   (2)

(b) Calculate the mean and the variance of X   (5)

(c) Assuming that the sales on different days are independent, use a suitable approximation to calculate the probability that the total amount sold in a 100 day period exceeds 250,000 litres.   (4)

10. (A3 1997) A lady has five coins in her purse, two 2p coins, two 5p coins and one 10p coin. She chooses three of the coins at random without replacement.

(a) Find the sampling distribution of T, the total value of the three chosen coins.   (4)

(b) Find E(T).   (2)

11. (A3 1998) A box contains six balls numbered 1, 2, 3, 4, 5, 6 respectively. Two balls are selected at random, simultaneously, and M denotes the larger of the two numbers obtained.

(a) Show that $P(M = 5) = \dfrac{4}{15}$.   (2)

(b) Construct a table showing the sampling distribution of M.   (3)

(c) Calculate E(M).   (2)

12. (A3 1998) When n randomly chosen numbers are rounded to the nearest integer the errors introduced X_1, X_2, ..., X_n can be regarded as a random sample from the continuous uniform distribution U(−0.5,0.5). Let $\overline{X}$ denote the sample mean.

(a) Find the variance of $\overline{X}$ in terms of n.   (2)

(b) Assuming that n is large, state an approximate distribution for $\overline{X}$. (1)

(c) Hence find the minimum value of n for which

$$P(-0.1 < \overline{X} < 0.1) > 0.95.$$ (4)

13. (S2 1998) A fair die has three of its faces numbered 1, two numbered 2, and the remaining face numbered 3. The die is to be thrown twice. Let Y denote the ratio of the higher score thrown to the lower score thrown. (For example, if the scores are 3,2 in any order then Y has the value $\frac{3}{2} = 1.5$ and if the scores are 2,2 then Y has the value $\frac{2}{2} = 1$.)

By first listing all possible pairs of scores that may be obtained, or otherwise, determine the sampling distribution of Y. (7)

Chapter 2

Point estimation of a population parameter

Introduction

Consider a random variable X whose distribution involves an unknown parameter θ. The success probability θ of a binomial distribution, the mean μ and standard deviation σ of a normal distribution are examples of parameters. As indicated in Chapter 1, an estimate of an unknown parameter θ can be obtained by taking a random sample of observations of the random variable and choosing a statistic which is thought to be appropriate for providing a sensible estimate. Denoting the random sample of observations by $X_1, X_2, \ldots, X_n$, let $T \equiv T(X_1, X_2, \ldots, X_n)$ be the statistic chosen to estimate θ. For example, as indicated in Chapter 3 of the S2 book, an intuitively sensible choice of statistic for estimating a population mean is the sample mean $\overline{X}$. The chosen statistic T is referred to as a **point estimator** of θ since it will provide a single value as an estimate of θ. Denoting the observed sample values by $x_1, x_2, \ldots, x_n$, the observed value of T is $t = T(x_1, x_2, \ldots, x_n)$, which is referred to as a **point estimate** of θ. Having chosen a sensible T for estimating θ how do we assess if it is a good estimator? What properties should T have for it to be regarded as a good estimator of θ? To answer these questions we need to look at the sampling distribution of T. One particular property of T that we shall regard as desirable is that of **unbiasedness**.

Definition. The statistic T is said to be an **unbiased estimator** of the parameter θ if and only if $E(T) = \theta$, whatever the value of θ.

Thus, T is an unbiased estimator of θ if the mean value of T over all possible samples of size n is equal to θ. The observed value t of T for a given sample is said to be an **unbiased estimate** of θ. Note that t is a randomly observed value of T.

In many situations it is possible to find more than one unbiased estimator of a parameter. The question then arises as to which is the better one to use. One obvious answer is to choose the one that is most likely to give a value close to the actual value of θ. Let T_1 and T_2 denote two unbiased estimators of θ. Since $E(T_1) = E(T_2) = \theta$, the standard deviations of their sampling distributions will indicate their relative degrees of concentration around θ. It follows that the better one is the one with the smaller standard deviation. This is illustrated in Figure 2.1, which shows the sampling distributions of two unbiased estimators of θ. It is clear from the diagram that T_1 is more likely than T_2 to have a value close to θ and, consequently, T_1 should be preferred to T_2. The standard deviation of the sampling distribution of an unbiased estimator T is called the **standard error** of T, and will abbreviated to SE(T).

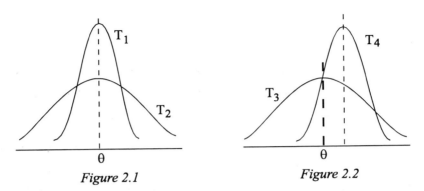

| Figure 2.1 | Figure 2.2 |

Note that the standard error is appropriate for choosing between unbiased estimators but is not appropriate for choosing between estimators not all of which are unbiased. Figure 2.2 shows the sampling distributions of two estimators T_3 and T_4, of which only T_3 is unbiased. In this case it is difficult to decide which of T_3 and T_4 is the more likely to have a value close to θ.

In the sections that follow we shall derive unbiased estimators for a population mean, a population variance, and the parameter (success probability) of a binomial distribution.

2.1 Point estimation of a population mean

Let $X_1, X_2, \ldots, X_n$ denote a random sample of n observations of a random variable X whose mean is μ and whose standard deviation is σ. As indicated earlier, a sensible choice of statistic for estimating μ is the sample mean $\overline{X}$. In Section 1.3.1 we showed that the sampling distribution of $\overline{X}$ has mean μ; that is, $E(\overline{X}) = \mu$, so that $\overline{X}$ is an unbiased estimator of μ. But we also know that $E(X_i) = \mu$ for every $i = 1, 2, \ldots, n$, so that each X_i is also an unbiased estimator of μ. Furthermore, if $\overline{X}_{(r)}$ is the mean of any r of the X_i, then $E(\overline{X}_{(r)}) = \mu$, so that $\overline{X}_{(r)}$ is also an unbiased estimator of μ for any $r = 2, 3, \ldots, n$.

It may be argued that $\overline{X}$ is the best choice from these unbiased estimators of μ because its value depends on all n observations. A stronger argument for preferring $\overline{X}$ is that its variance (and therefore its standard error) is smaller than the variance of any of the other possible unbiased estimators. From Section 1.3.1., the variances are :

$$\mathrm{Var}(X_i) = \sigma^2, \quad \mathrm{Var}(\overline{X}_{(r)}) = \sigma^2/r, \quad \mathrm{Var}(\overline{X}) = \sigma^2/n.$$

In fact, it may be shown that of all possible linear combinations of a random sample of n observations the sample mean is the one with the smallest variance. (You are asked to prove this for n = 2 in Question 2 of Exercises 2.1.)

In addition we note that the larger the value of n the better the estimator $\overline{X}$, since its variance decreases as n increases.

Example 1

Let X_1, X_2, and X_3 denote a random sample of three observations of a random variable X whose mean is μ and whose standard deviation is σ. Show that the two statistics

$$T_1 = \frac{1}{6}(X_1 + 2X_2 + 3X_3) \text{ and } T_2 = \frac{1}{5}(X_1 + 2X_2 + 2X_3)$$

are both unbiased estimators of μ and determine which of them is the better estimator. Write down the linear combination of X_1, X_2, and X_3 which will give an unbiased estimator of μ with minimum standard error. Express this minimum standard error as a multiple of σ.

Solution

Since X_1, X_2, and X_3 are random observations we know that they are independent and that each has the same distribution as X. In particular, $E(X_1) = E(X_2) = E(X_3) = \mu$ and $\mathrm{Var}(X_1) = \mathrm{Var}(X_2) = \mathrm{Var}(X_3) = \sigma^2$. Using properties of expectation we have

$$E(T_1) = \frac{1}{6}[E(X_1) + 2E(X_2) + 3E(X_3)] = \frac{1}{6} \times 6\mu = \mu,$$

so that T_1 is an unbiased estimator of μ. Similarly we have

$$E(T_2) = \frac{1}{5}[E(X_1) + 2E(X_2) + 2E(X_3)] = \frac{1}{5} \times 5\mu = \mu,$$

showing that T_2 is also an unbiased estimator of μ.

Using properties of variance we find that

$$\mathrm{Var}(T_1) = \frac{1}{36}[\mathrm{Var}(X_1) + 4\mathrm{Var}(X_2) + 9\mathrm{Var}(X_3)] = \frac{1}{36} \times 14\sigma^2 \cong 0.3889\sigma^2$$

and $\quad \mathrm{Var}(T_2) = \frac{1}{25}[\mathrm{Var}(X_1) + 4\mathrm{Var}(X_2) + 4\mathrm{Var}(X_3)] = \frac{1}{25} \times 9\sigma^2 \cong 0.36\sigma^2$

Since $\mathrm{Var}(T_2)$ is $< \mathrm{Var}(T_1)$, T_2 is the better estimator of μ.

As stated prior to this example, the linear combination of a random sample of observations which is the unbiased estimator of μ with the smallest variance is the sample mean. Thus, in this example the best linear combination to take is $\overline{X} = \frac{1}{3}(X_1 + X_2 + X_3)$, whose variance is $\sigma^2/3$ and whose standard error is $\sigma/\sqrt{3}$.

Example 2

The random variable X has probability density function f given by

$$f(x) = \theta x + \frac{3}{2}x^2, \qquad \text{for } -1 \le x \le 1.$$

where θ is an unknown constant.

(a) Show that $E(X) = \frac{2}{3}\theta$.

(b) Let $\overline{X}$ denote the mean of a random sample of n observations of X. Find a multiple of $\overline{X}$ that is an unbiased estimator of θ. Express the variance of this estimator in terms of θ and n.

Solution

(a) $E(X) = \int_{-1}^{1} \left(\theta x^2 + \frac{3}{2}x^3\right) dx = \left[\frac{1}{3}\theta x^3 + \frac{3}{8}x^4\right]_{-1}^{1} = \frac{2}{3}\theta.$

(b) Hence $E(\overline{X}) = \frac{2}{3}\theta$, from which we deduce that $E\left(\frac{3}{2}\overline{X}\right) = \theta$. That is, $\frac{3}{2}\overline{X}$ is an unbiased estimator of θ.

We know that $\quad \text{Var}\left(\frac{3}{2}\overline{X}\right) = \frac{9}{4}\text{Var}(\overline{X}) = \frac{9}{4n}\text{Var}(X).$

$$E(X^2) = \int_{-1}^{1}\left(\theta x^3 + \frac{3}{2}x^4\right)dx = \left[\frac{1}{4}\theta x^4 + \frac{3}{10}x^5\right]_{-1}^{1} = \frac{3}{5}$$

Thus $\quad\quad\quad \text{Var}(X) = \frac{3}{5} - \left(\frac{2}{3}\theta\right)^2 = \frac{27-20\theta^2}{45}$

and the variance of our unbiased estimator of θ is

$$\text{Var}\left(\frac{3}{2}\overline{X}\right) = \frac{9}{4n}\times\frac{27-20\theta^2}{45} = \frac{27-20\theta^2}{20n}.$$

Exercise 2.1

1. Let X_1, X_2, and X_3 denote a random sample of three observations of a random variable X whose mean is μ and whose standard deviation is 4. Show that each of the statistics $\quad T_1 = X_1 + X_2 - X_3, \quad T_2 = \frac{1}{4}(2X_1 + X_2 + X_3), \quad T_3 = \frac{1}{3}(X_1 + X_2 + X_3)$

is an unbiased estimator of μ and determine which of them has the smallest variance.

2. A statistic of the form $T = aX_1 + bX_2$, where a and b are constants and X_1 and X_2 are independent observations of a random variable X having mean μ and standard deviation σ, is to be used as an unbiased estimator of μ. Find an equation connecting a and b for T to be unbiased. Write down an expression for the variance of T in terms of a, b and σ.

Hence find the values of a and b for which T is an unbiased estimator of μ having the smallest possible standard error.

3. Let $\overline{X}$ denote the mean of a random sample of n observations of the random variable X which has the uniform distribution over the interval $[0, \theta]$, where θ is unknown. Find the value of c if $T = c\overline{X}$ is to be an unbiased estimator of θ. Also find the variance of this estimator in terms of θ and n.

4. Let X denote a random observation from a distribution having mean μ and standard deviation 4, and let Y denote a random observation from another distribution having mean 2μ and standard deviation 8. Given that the observed values of X and Y were 10 and 28, respectively, obtain the best unbiased estimate of μ and explain in what sense it is best.

5. A random sample of 8 observations from a Poisson distribution had the values

$$3, \ 0, \ 4, \ 1, \ 2, \ 1, \ 3, \ 1$$

Calculate the best unbiased estimate of the mean of the distribution.

6. Steel bearings have diameters that are normally distributed with mean μ mm and standard deviation 0.03 mm. A random sample of nine bearings had diameters (in mm)

$$5.01, \ 5.03, \ 4.96, \ 4.91, \ 5.06, \ 4.97, \ 5.02, \ 4.94, \ 4.92$$

(a) Calculate the best unbiased estimate of μ and write down the value of the standard error of the estimator.

(b) Calculate the probability that another random sample of nine bearings will have a mean diameter within 0.01 mm of μ.

7. The random variable X is distributed with probability density function f, where

$$f(x) \ = \ 3x^2/\theta^3, \qquad \text{for } 0 \leq x \leq \theta.$$

If X_1 and X_2 are two independent observations of X show that $T = \dfrac{2}{3}(X_1 + X_2)$ is an unbiased estimator of θ and determine its standard error in terms of θ.

8. Let X_1, X_2, and X_3 denote three independent observations of the random variable X whose mean is $\dfrac{1}{2}\theta$ and whose variance is $\dfrac{1}{12}\theta^2$. Find the value of c for $T = c(X_1 + X_2 + X_3)$ to be an unbiased estimator of θ and determine its standard error in terms of θ.

9. Given that $\overline{X}$ is the mean of a random sample of n observations from the uniform distribution $U[0, \theta]$ find an unbiased estimator of θ. A random sample of 10 observations had the values $\ \ 1.6, \ 1.8, \ 2.1, \ 4.4, \ 1.8, \ 2.0, \ 1.9, \ 1.7, \ 2.0, \ 2.0$

Calculate an unbiased estimate of θ. Give a reason why this estimate cannot possibly be the true value of θ.

2.2 Point estimation of a probability

Let X denote the number of successes that will be obtained in n independent Bernoulli trials in each of which the probability of a success is θ (unknown). We know that $X \sim B(n, \theta)$. The proportion of successes in the n trials is $P = X/n$ and is an intuitively sensible statistic for estimating θ. In Section 1.4 we showed that the sampling distribution of P was such that

$$E(P) = \theta, \tag{1}$$

so that P is an unbiased estimator of θ. We also showed that $Var(P) = \theta(1 - \theta)/n$, so that the standard error of P is given by

$$SE(P) = \sqrt{\left\{ \frac{\theta(1-\theta)}{n} \right\}} \tag{2}$$

As was the case for $\overline{X}$ we see that the larger the value of n the better the estimator in the sense that its standard error decreases as n increases.

Since SE(P) involves θ whose value is not known it is not possible to evaluate it even after the observed value p of P becomes available. However, we can get some idea of the value of SE(P) as follows.

$$\theta(1 - \theta) = \theta - \theta^2 \equiv \frac{1}{4} - \left(\frac{1}{2} - \theta \right)^2,$$

from which it follows that the maximum value of $\theta(1-\theta)$ is $\frac{1}{4}$, which occurs when $\theta = \frac{1}{2}$.

Hence, for any θ,

$$SE(P) \leq \frac{1}{2\sqrt{n}} \tag{3}$$

Furthermore, the graph of $\theta(1 - \theta)$ is fairly flat in the neighbourhood of $\theta = \frac{1}{2}$, so that the right-hand side of (3) provides a useful approximation to SE(P) for any θ that does not differ very much from $\frac{1}{2}$. Another approximation to SE(P) is also possible after the trials have been performed. If the observed number of successes is x then the corresponding value of P is $p = x/n$ which can then be substituted for θ in (2) for an estimate of SE(P) given by

$$ESE(P) = \sqrt{\frac{p(1-p)}{n}} \tag{4}$$

where ESE(P) is our abbreviation for an estimate of the standard error of P.

The above results are also valid in the case where θ is the proportion of the objects in a collection of N objects which have a particular attribute and P denotes the proportion of the objects having this attribute in a random sample of n objects drawn **with replacement** from the collection. If the sampling is done without replacement then the above results will be approximately true provided n is very much smaller than N, since then the probability of having an object with the attribute is roughly constant from one draw to the next.

Example 1

In order to predict the proportion of all the votes that will be cast for a particular candidate in a forthcoming election, a random sample of 100 voters was canvassed and 38 of them stated that they intended voting for the candidate. Calculate an unbiased estimate of the proportion of all voters who intend to vote for the candidate. Find (a) an upper bound, (b) an approximate value, for the standard error of the estimator used.

Solution

It is reasonable to assume that the total number of voters is extremely large so that the results of this section can be used.

The observed proportion of the sampled voters who intend to vote for the candidate is

$$p = \frac{38}{100} = 0.38,$$

which from (1), is an unbiased estimate of the proportion θ of all the voters who intend to vote for the candidate. (We are, of course, assuming that the sampled voters answered truthfully!).

(a) From (3) with n = 100 the upper bound for the standard error SE(P) of our estimator is

$$\frac{1}{2\sqrt{100}} = \frac{1}{20} = 0.05.$$

(b) From (4) with n = 100 and p = 0.38 an approximation to SE(P) is given by

$$ESE(P) = \sqrt{\left(\frac{0.38 \times 0.62}{100}\right)} = 0.0485.$$

Example 2

The random variable X has probability density function f, where

$$f(x) = \theta x + \frac{3}{2}x^2, \quad \text{for } -1 \le x \le 1$$

Let Y denote the number of positive values in a random sample of n observations of X. Find, in terms of Y, an unbiased estimator of θ and obtain an expression for its variance in terms of θ.

Solution

From the definition of Y we know that Y ~ B(n, p), where

$$p = P(X > 0) = \int_0^1 \left(\theta x + \frac{3}{2}x^2\right)dx = \left[\frac{1}{2}\theta x^2 + \frac{1}{2}x^3\right]_0^1 = \frac{1}{2}\theta + \frac{1}{2}.$$

29

Hence, $E(Y) = np = \dfrac{n\theta}{2} + \dfrac{n}{2}$

from which it follows that

$$\dfrac{2}{n}\left(E(Y) - \dfrac{n}{2}\right) = \theta, \text{ or equivalently } E\left(\dfrac{2Y}{n} - 1\right) = \theta$$

Thus, $\qquad T = \dfrac{2Y}{n} - 1$ is an unbiased estimator of θ.

The variance of T is

$$Var(T) = \dfrac{4}{n^2}Var(Y) = \dfrac{4}{n^2} \times np(1-p) = \dfrac{4}{n}\left(\dfrac{1}{2}\theta + \dfrac{1}{2}\right)\left(-\dfrac{1}{2}\theta + \dfrac{1}{2}\right) = \dfrac{1-\theta^2}{n}.$$

Exercise 2.2

1. Fifty tosses of a damaged coin resulted in 30 heads and 20 tails. Calculate an unbiased estimate of the probability of obtaining a head in a single toss of this coin. Also calculate an estimate of the standard error of your estimator and the maximum possible value of this standard error.

2. A random sample of 100 mass-produced items was found to contain two defectives. Estimate the proportion of all such items that will be defective. Calculate an estimate of the standard error of your estimator and obtain an upper bound for the value of this standard error.

3. In a random sample of 200 customers at a supermarket it was found that 120 of them had spent more than £20. Estimate the proportion of all the customers at this supermarket who will spend more than £20 there, and obtain an upper bound for the standard error of your estimator.

4. Two pupils conducted experiments to estimate the probability θ that a particular type of drawing pin would alight point upwards when thrown onto a hard surface. The first pupil threw the drawing pin 300 times and the second threw it 200 times. Let X_1 denote the number of throws by the first pupil that resulted in the drawing pin alighting point upwards, and let X_2 denote the number of throws by the second pupil that resulted in the drawing pin alighting point upwards. Show that

$$T_1 = (2X_1 + 3X_2)/1200 \quad \text{and} \quad T_2 = (X_1 + X_2)/500$$

are both unbiased estimators of θ. Determine which of them is the better estimator.

5. It is known that the two mutually exclusive events A and B are equally likely to occur in any trial of a random experiment; denote their common probability by θ. The following two methods have been proposed for estimating θ.

METHOD 1. Conduct 20 independent trials, record the number R of occasions that A occurs and take $T_1 = R/20$ to be the estimator of θ.

METHOD 2. Conduct 10 independent trials, record the number S of occasions when either A or B occurs and take $T_2 = S/20$ to be the estimator of θ.

Show that both T_1 and T_2 are unbiased estimators of θ. Determine the variances of T_1 and T_2 and state, with your reason, which estimator you would choose.

6. A firm produces items which are classified as either defective or perfect. From time to time the firm is required to take a random sample and estimate the proportion of defectives produced. A legal requirement is that the estimator should have a variance no greater than 0.001. Show that this can always be achieved (whatever the proportion of defectives being produced at the time) with a sample size of 250.

7. A coin when tossed has probability p of falling heads. In order to estimate the probability θ of obtaining two heads in two tosses the coin is tossed n times ($n \geq 2$). If X heads are obtained in the n tosses show that $T = X(X - 1)/n(n - 1)$ is an unbiased estimator of θ. Deduce an unbiased estimator for the probability of obtaining two tails in two tosses of the coin.

8. The random variable X takes the values 1, 2 and 3 with respective probabilities θ, 2θ, and $1 - 3\theta$, where $0 < \theta < 1/3$. In order to estimate θ a random sample of n observations of X are taken. If the values 1, 2, 3 occur X_1, X_2, X_3 times respectively, show that the following estimators of θ are all unbiased :

$$T_1 = \frac{X_1}{n}, \quad T_2 = \frac{X_2}{2n}, \quad T_3 = \frac{1}{3}\left(1 - \frac{X_3}{n}\right)$$

Show that, of these three estimators, T_3 has the smallest standard error for all permissible values of θ.

9. A production process produces bags of sugar, each nominally containing 1 kg. Past experience shows that the actual amount contained per bag is normally distributed with standard deviation 3 g. When a bag is tested it is rejected if it is found to contain less than 992 g. An estimate of the probability θ that a randomly selected bag will be rejected is required. A random sample of 20 bags gave a mean content of 998.5 g. Find a sensible estimate of the value of θ. (It is not advisable here to try to find an unbiased estimate.)

2.3 Point estimation of a population variance

Let X_1, X_2, . . ., X_n denote a random sample of n observations of a random variable X having unknown mean μ and unknown variance σ^2. An estimate of σ^2 is required. Since $\sigma^2 = E[(X - \mu)^2]$ is the mean value of $(X - \mu)^2$, this suggests that we should consider the mean value of $(X_i - \overline{X})^2$ as an estimator of σ^2; that is consider

$$T = \frac{1}{n}\Sigma(X_i - \overline{X})^2 \tag{1}$$

the summation being from i = 1 to i = n. To determine whether T is an unbiased estimator of σ^2 let us first evaluate $E[\Sigma(X_i - \overline{X})^2]$.

On expanding we have

$$\Sigma(X_i - \overline{X})^2 = \Sigma X_i^2 - 2\overline{X}\,\Sigma X_i + n\overline{X}^2$$
$$= \Sigma X_i^2 - n\overline{X}^2, \text{ since } \Sigma X_i = n\overline{X}.$$

Hence $E[\Sigma(X_i - \overline{X})^2] = \Sigma E(X_i^2) - nE(\overline{X}^2)$

Since each X_i has the same distribution as X

$$E(X_i^2) = Var(X_i) + [E(X_i)]^2 = \sigma^2 + \mu^2.$$

Also, from Section 1.3.1, we know that $E(\overline{X}) = \mu$ and $Var(\overline{X}) = \sigma^2/n$, so that

$$E(\overline{X}^2) = Var(\overline{X}) + [E(\overline{X})]^2 = \frac{\sigma^2}{n} + \mu^2.$$

It follows that

$$E[\Sigma(X_i - \overline{X})^2] = n(\sigma^2 + \mu^2) - n\left(\frac{\sigma^2}{n} + \mu^2\right) = (n-1)\sigma^2.$$

Consequently for an unbiased estimator of σ^2 we should use the statistic

$$\frac{1}{n-1}\Sigma(X_i - \overline{X})^2$$

and not T as given in (1). We shall refer to this statistic as the **sample unbiased estimator** of σ^2 and it will be denoted by S^2. Therefore, the unbiased estimator of σ^2 is

$$S^2 = \frac{1}{n-1}\Sigma(X_i - \overline{X})^2 \tag{2}$$

Given the sample values $x_1, x_2, \ldots, x_n$,

$$s^2 = \frac{1}{n-1}\Sigma(x_i - \overline{x})^2 \equiv \frac{1}{n-1}[\Sigma x_i^2 - n\overline{x}^2] \tag{3}$$

is the sample unbiased estimate of σ^2.

[Note that, although S^2 is an unbiased estimator of σ^2, it does not follow that S is an unbiased estimator of σ. It is, however, sensible to use S as an estimate of σ although the resulting estimate will be biased.]

Example 1

A random sample of 10 observations of a random variable X had the values

2.36, 2.43, 2.31, 2.41, 2.39 2.42, 2.39, 2.41, 2.37, 2.38

Calculate an unbiased estimate of the variance of X.

Solution

Denoting the observed values by $x_1, x_2, \ldots, x_{10}$ we find that

$$\overline{x} = 23.87/10 = 2.387 \text{ and } \Sigma x_i^2 = 56.9887.$$

Using (3) the required unbiased estimate of the variance of X is
$$s^2 = \frac{1}{9}(56.9887 - 10 \times 2.387^2) = 0.001223 \text{ to 4 significant figures.}$$

Example 2

The random variable X has the probability density function f given by
$$f(x) = 2x/\theta^2, \qquad \text{for } 0 \leq x \leq \theta.$$
A random sample of 5 observations of X had the values 0.6, 1.5, 0.8, 1.1 and 1.3.
Evaluate Var(X) and hence find an unbiased estimate of θ^2.

Solution

It is left as an exercise to verify that
$$E(X) = \frac{2}{3}\theta \quad \text{and} \quad Var(X) = \frac{1}{18}\theta^2.$$
From (3) the sample unbiased estimate of Var(X) is
$$s^2 = \frac{1}{4}\{\Sigma x^2 - n\bar{x}^2\} = \frac{1}{4}\{6.15 - 5 \times (1.06)^2\} = 0.133.$$
Hence, an unbiased estimate of $\theta^2 = 18$ Var(X) is
$$18s^2 = 18 \times 0.133 = 2.394$$

Exercise 2.3

1. A random sample of 8 observations of a random variable X had the values
$$3.7, \ 3.4, \ 4.2, \ 3.9, \ 3.7, \ 3.2, \ 4.0, \ 4.3$$
Calculate unbiased estimates of the mean and the variance of X.

2. The operational lifetimes, in hours, of a random sample of 5 electric light bulbs of a particular brand were :
$$1641, \ 1519, \ 1621, \ 1586, \ 1563$$
Calculate an unbiased estimate of the variance of the operational lifetimes of such light bulbs.

3. A random sample of 20 observations of a random variable X had values (x) such that
$$\Sigma x = 38.6 \quad \text{and} \ \Sigma x^2 = 96.88.$$
(a) Calculate unbiased estimates of the mean and the variance of X.
(b) Given that $X \sim U[0, \theta]$, where θ is unknown, deduce unbiased estimates of (i) θ and (ii) θ^2.

4. A random sample of 10 observations from a Poisson distribution had values such that they summed to 33 and the sum of their squares was 144. Calculate TWO unbiased estimates of the mean of the Poisson distribution.

5. Let X_1, X_2, . . ., X_n denote a random sample of n observations of a random variable whose mean is 20.

(a) Show that the statistic

$$T_1 = \frac{1}{n} \sum_{i=1}^{n} (X_i - 20)^2$$

is an unbiased estimator of Var(X).

(b) Find the value of the constant c for the statistic

$$T_2 = c \sum_{i=1}^{n-1} (X_{i+1} - X_i)^2$$

to be an unbiased estimator of Var(X).

6. An unbiased estimator is required for $\lambda = 4\mu + \mu^2$, where μ is the mean of a Poisson distribution. Given that X_1, X_2, . . ., X_n are independent observations from the Poisson distribution, show that the statistic

$$T = 3 \overline{X} + \frac{1}{n} \sum_{i=1}^{n} X_i^2$$

is an unbiased estimator of λ.

2.4 Further examples on unbiased estimation

Example 1

A random sample of n observations from a population distribution whose mean μ is unknown and whose standard deviation is known to be 1, is to be used to estimate the value of μ^2. Show that $\overline{X}^2$, where $\overline{X}$ is the sample mean, is a biased estimator of μ^2. Deduce an unbiased estimator of μ^2 in terms of $\overline{X}$ and n.

Solution

We know that the sampling distribution of $\overline{X}$ is such that

$$E(\overline{X}) = \mu \text{ and } Var(\overline{X}) = \frac{\sigma^2}{n} = \frac{1}{n}$$

Now $$E(\overline{X}^2) = Var(\overline{X}) + [E(\overline{X})]^2 = \frac{1}{n} + \mu^2$$

which shows that $\overline{X}^2$ is a biased estimator of μ^2. Rearranging this result we have

$$E(\overline{X}^2) - \frac{1}{n} = \mu^2, \text{ or } E\left(\overline{X}^2 - \frac{1}{n}\right) = \mu^2,$$

from which it follows that

$$T = \overline{X}^2 - \frac{1}{n} \quad \text{is an unbiased estimator of } \mu^2.$$

[Since $\overline{X}$ is an unbiased estimator of μ one's intuition would have suggested that $\overline{X}^2$ should be an unbiased estimator of μ^2 but this is not so. However, notice that the actual bias is small when n is large.]

Example 2

An instrument for measuring the length of a line is such that the recorded value for a line of length a cm is equally likely to be any value in the interval (a − c, a + c), where c (< a) is a known positive constant. The instrument is used to obtain two independent observations, X_1 and X_2, of the length a of a side of a square. The following two methods have been proposed for estimating the area $A = a^2$ of the square.

Method 1. Estimate A using $T_1 = X_1 X_2$.

Method 2. Estimate A using $T_2 = \dfrac{1}{4}(X_1 + X_2)^2$.

Show that Method 1 is the only one of these that will give an unbiased estimate of A, and determine the standard error of this estimator in terms of a and c.

Solution

Since X_1 and X_2 are independent, on using properties of expectation we get

$$E(T_1) = E(X_1)E(X_2)$$

and $\qquad E(T_2) = \dfrac{1}{4}\{E(X_1{}^2) + 2E(X_1)E(X_2) + E(X_2{}^2)\}$

Let X cm denote the recorded length of a line of true length a cm. From the given information $X \sim U(a - c, a + c)$ and each of X_1 and X_2 has this distribution. Hence

$$E(X_1) = E(X_2) = E(X) = \dfrac{1}{2}[(a + c) + (a - c)] = a,$$

$$E(X_1{}^2) = E(X_2{}^2) = E(X^2) = \operatorname{Var}(X) + [E(X)]^2$$
$$= \dfrac{1}{12}[(a + c) - (a - c)]^2 + a^2 = \dfrac{1}{3}(c^2 + 3a^2).$$

Using these results we obtain

$$E(T_1) = a \times a = a^2,$$

from which we deduce that Method 1 will give an unbiased estimate of the area of the square. Also

$$E(T_2) = \dfrac{1}{4}\left\{\dfrac{1}{3}\left(c^2 + 3a^2\right) + 2 \times a \times a + \dfrac{1}{3}\left(c^2 + 3a^2\right)\right\} = a^2 + \dfrac{1}{6}c^2,$$

from which it follows that Method 2 will not give an unbiased estimate of the area of the square.

To find the standard error of T_1 let us first find $\operatorname{Var}(T_1)$. We have

$$\operatorname{Var}(T_1) = E(T_1{}^2) - [E(T_1)]^2 = E(T_1{}^2) - a^4.$$

$$= E(X_1{}^2)E(X_2{}^2) - a^4 = \frac{1}{9}(c^2 + 3a^2)^2 - a^4 = \frac{1}{9}c^2(c^2 + 6a^2).$$

Hence, the standard error of T_1 is

$$SE(T_1) = \frac{1}{3}c\sqrt{\left(c^2 + 6a^2\right)}.$$

Exercise 2.4

1. The random variable X has probability density function f given by

$$f(x) = \frac{1}{2}(1 + \theta x), \qquad \text{for} - 1 < x < 1,$$

where θ is a constant such that $-1 < \theta < 1$.

(a) Let R denote the number of positive values in a random sample of n observations of X. Show that

$$T_1 = \frac{4R}{n} - 2$$

is an unbiased estimator of θ and determine its variance.

(b) Let $\overline{X}$ denote the mean of a random sample of n observations of X. Show that $T_2 = 3\overline{X}$ is also an unbiased estimator of θ and determine its variance.

(c) State, with your reason, which is the better of the two estimators.

2. The random variable X can take only the values 1, 2 and 3, their respective probabilities being θ, θ and $1 - 2\theta$, where $0 < \theta < \frac{1}{2}$. In a random sample of n observations of X let $\overline{X}$ denote the sample mean and let R denote the number of 3's obtained. Show that

$$T_1 = 1 - \frac{\overline{X}}{3} \quad \text{and} \quad T_2 = \frac{1}{2}\left(1 - \frac{R}{n}\right)$$

are both unbiased estimators of θ. Determine which of the two estimators has the smaller standard error.

3. The random variable X can take only the values 0, 1 and 2 with respective probabilities $\frac{1}{2}\theta$, $1 - \theta$ and $\frac{1}{2}\theta$. Let X_1 and X_2 denote two randomly observed values of X. List the possible values of $\{X_1, X_2\}$ that may arise and calculate the probability of each possibility. By calculating the value of $(X_1 - X_2)^2$ for each possible $\{X_1, X_2\}$ determine the sampling distribution of $(X_1 - X_2)^2$. Hence show that $T_1 = (X_1 - X_2)^2/2$ is an unbiased estimator of θ and express it variance in terms of θ.

Since $\theta = P(X \neq 1)$, another possible estimator of θ is the proportion of observed values not equal to 1; this estimator is given by $T_2 = \frac{N}{2}$, where N is the number of the two observations not equal to 1. Show that T_2 is an unbiased estimator of θ. Determine which of T_1 and T_2 is the better estimator of θ.

4. The number of telephone calls, X, into an office in a period of t minutes has the Poisson distribution with mean $t\theta$, where $\theta > 0$ is unknown.

(a) Write down an expression, in terms of t and θ, for $E(X)$.

(b) Let X_1 and X_2 denote the numbers of calls that will be made to the office in two independent time intervals of durations t_1 and t_2 minutes, where $t_1 \neq t_2$.

Show that $T = (X_1 - X_2)/(t_1 - t_2)$ is an unbiased estimator of θ. By considering possible values that T may take explain why T may yield an unsatisfactory estimate of θ.

5. A random variable X can take the values 2, 3 and 4 with probabilities 0.2, 0.4 and 0.4 respectively. Find the sampling distribution of $\overline{X}$, the mean of a random sample of two observations of X. Hence, determine whether or not

(a) $\overline{X}$ is an unbiased estimator of $\mu = E(X)$,

(b) $1/\overline{X}$ is an unbiased estimator of $1/\mu$,

6. Let X_1, X_2, . . ., X_n denote a random sample of n observations from a Poisson distribution having mean μ. Show that

$$T = \frac{1}{n}\sum_{i=1}^{n} X_i^2 - \frac{1}{n}\sum_{i=1}^{n} X_i$$

is an unbiased estimator of μ^2.

7. The random variable X has probability density function f given by

$$f(x) = \alpha(\alpha + 1)x^{\alpha-1}(1 - x), \qquad \text{for } 0 \leq x \leq 1.$$

If X_1, X_2, . . ., X_n are a random sample of n observations of X show that

$$T = \frac{1}{n}\sum_{i=1}^{n} \frac{X_i}{1 - X_i}$$

is an unbiased estimator of α.

Miscellaneous Questions on Chapter 2

1. (1988) The random variables X and Y are independent, with X having mean μ and variance σ^2 and Y having mean μ and variance σ^2/k, where k is a positive constant. Let $\overline{X}$ denote the mean of a random sample of 10 observations of X, and let $\overline{Y}$ denote the mean of a random sample of 15 observations of Y. Show that

$$T_1 = \frac{\left(2\overline{X} + 3k\overline{Y}\right)}{2 + 3k} \quad \text{and} \quad T_2 = \frac{2\overline{X} + 3\overline{Y}}{5}$$

are both unbiased estimators of μ. (3)

Find expressions for the variances of T_1 and T_2, and show that the variance of T_1 is less than or equal to the variance of T_2. (6)

Find in terms of k, the value a for which
$$T = a\overline{X} + (1-a)\overline{Y}$$
has smallest possible variance. (6)

2. (1989) Let X denote the number of successes that will be obtained in n independent trials in each of which the probability of a success is p. If $n \geq 2$ and $0 < p < 1$ show that only one of the two statistics
$$T_1 = \left(\frac{X}{n}\right)^2 \quad \text{and} \quad T_2 = \frac{X(X-1)}{n(n-1)}$$
is an unbiased estimator of p^2. (5)

3. (1990) The continuous random variable X is distributed with probability density function f given by
$$f(x) = \frac{1}{2}x^2 + \frac{1}{3}\theta x + \frac{1}{3}, \quad \text{for} -1 < x < 1$$
$$f(x) = 0, \qquad\qquad\qquad \text{otherwise,}$$
where $0 \leq \theta \leq 2$.

(a) Show that $E(X) = 2\theta/9$. (2)

(b) Express $P(X > 0)$ in terms of θ. (2)

(c) For a random sample of n observations of X, let $\overline{X}$ denote the sample mean and let Y denote the number of observations that are positive. Show that
$$T_1 = \frac{9}{2}\overline{X} \quad \text{and} \quad T_2 = \frac{6}{n}Y - 3$$
are both unbiased estimators of θ. (5)

(d) Determine which of T_1 and T_2 is the better estimator of θ. (6)

4. (1991) In the triangle ABC, angle $ACB = 90°$, angle $BAC = \alpha°$, and angle $ABC = \beta°$ $= (90 - \alpha)°$. Independent measurements are made of α and β. Let X and Y denote the measured values of α and β, respectively. It is known that X and Y are normally distributed with standard deviation σ and means α and β, respectively.

(a) Calculate, correct to two decimal places, the probability that $X + Y$ will have a value which differs from 90 by less than σ. (3)

(b) Show that $T_1 = X + \frac{1}{2}(90 - X - Y)$ is an unbiased estimator of α. Verify that T_1 is better than X as an estimator of α. (5)

(c) Calculate, correct to three decimal places, the probability that $|T_1 - \alpha|$ will be less than σ. (3)

(d) Let $T_2 = Y + \frac{1}{2}(90 - X - Y)$. Show that $Var(T_1 - T_2) = 2[Var(T_1) + Var(T_2)]$ (4)

5. (1991) A computer file holds a very large number of TRUE/FALSE questions. In a random sample of 75 of the questions it was found that 60 were ones for which the correct answer is TRUE.

(a) Calculate an unbiased estimate of the proportion of all the questions for which the correct answer is TRUE.

(b) Calculate an estimate of the standard error of your estimate in (a).

(c) Calculate an unbiased estimator of the difference between the proportion of all the questions for which the correct answer is TRUE and the proportion for which the correct answer is FALSE.

(d) Calculate an estimate of the standard error of your estimate in (c). (6)

6. (1992) The continuous random variable X has probability density function f, where

$$f(x) = \frac{4x^3}{\alpha^4} \, , \qquad \text{for } 0 \le x \le \alpha,$$

$$f(x) = 0 \, , \qquad \text{otherwise.}$$

If $\overline{X}$ is the mean of a random sample of 24 observations of X show that $T = 5\overline{X}/4$ is an unbiased estimator of α. Express the standard error of T in terms of α. (6)

7. (1993) The measured length, X mm, of a line of true length μ mm is normally distributed with mean μ and standard deviation 0.5. Let X_1 mm and X_2 mm denote the measured lengths of two adjacent sides of a rectangle whose true dimensions are 12 mm by 8 mm. It may be assumed that X_1 and X_2 are independent. Show that X_1X_2 is an unbiased estimator of the area of the rectangle and evaluate its standard error correct to three decimal places. (6)

8. (1994) (a) A box contains 5 cards numbered 1, 2, 3, 4, 5 respectively. A random sample of three cards is selected without replacement. Write down, in a table, the 10 different possible samples of three numbers selected. Calculate the mean $\overline{X}$ and the median M for each sample. Hence determine the sampling distributions of $\overline{X}$ and M. (5)

(i) Verify that both $\overline{X}$ and M are unbiased estimators of the mean μ of the 5 numbers in the box. (3)

(ii) Calculate the variances of both $\overline{X}$ and M. State, with a reason, which of $\overline{X}$ and M you regard as the better estimator of μ. (3)

(b) Another box contains n cards numbered 1, 2, 3, . . ., n respectively. Three cards are selected at random without replacement and $\overline{X}$ denotes the mean of the three numbers on them. Assuming that $\overline{X}$ is an unbiased estimator of the mean of the n numbers in the box, show that $2\overline{X} - 1$ is an unbiased estimator of n. (2)

In a particular case, the numbers on the three cards were found to be 1, 2, 6. Use the above result to estimate n and comment on your result. (2)

9. (1995) The random variable X has probability density function
$$f(x) = \frac{1}{2} + \lambda x, \quad \text{for} -1 \le x \le 1,$$
$$f(x) = 0, \quad \text{otherwise,}$$
where λ is an unknown constant between $-\frac{1}{2}$ and $\frac{1}{2}$.

(a) Find E(X) in terms of λ and show that $Var(X) = (3 - 4\lambda^2)/9$. (4)

(b) Find $P(X > 0)$ in terms of λ (2)

In order to estimate λ, n independent observations are made on X. Y denotes the number of positive observations obtained and $\overline{X}$ denotes the sample mean.

(c) Name the distribution of Y and show that $T_1 = \frac{2Y}{n} - 1$ is an unbiased estimator of λ. (3)

(d) Given that $T_2 = k\,\overline{X}$ is another unbiased estimator of λ, find the value of k. (2)

(e) Write down an expression for $Var(T_2)$ in terms of λ and n and show that $Var(T_1) = (1 - \lambda^2)/n$. Hence determine, with a reason, which is the better estimator. (4)

10. (A3: 1996) The discrete random variable X takes the values 1, 2, 3 with probabilities θ, 2θ, $1 - 3\theta$ respectively.

(a) State the largest possible range for the constant θ. (1)

(b) Find E(X) in terms of θ and show that $Var(X) = 6\theta - 16\theta^2$ (4)

(c) To estimate θ, a random sample $X_1, X_2, \ldots, X_n$ of n observations on X is taken and $\overline{X}$ denotes the sample mean.

(i) Find the numerical values of a and b for which
$$\hat{\theta}_1 = a + b\overline{X}$$
is an unbiased estimator for θ. Show that the variance of this unbiased estimator

is $\quad \frac{1}{n}\left(\frac{3}{8}\theta - \theta^2\right)$ (5)

(ii) Given that N denotes the number of observations equal to 1, and that
$$\hat{\theta}_2 = cN$$
is another unbiased estimator or θ, find c in terms of n.
Find the variance of $\hat{\theta}_2$ in terms of n and θ. (3)

(ii) Determine which of $\hat{\theta}_1$, $\hat{\theta}_2$ is the better estimator for θ. (2)

11. (A3 1997) A factory produces a large number of screws of which an unknown proportion p are defective. In order to estimate p, random samples of 50 and 100 screws are taken from the production line at different times during each shift. The numbers of defective screws found in these samples are denoted by X and Y respectively.

Two possible estimators for p are considered

$$T_1 = \frac{1}{2}\left(\frac{X}{50} + \frac{Y}{100}\right) \text{ and } T_2 = \frac{X+Y}{150}.$$

(a) Show that both T_1 and T_2 are unbiased estimators for p. (4)

(b) Determine the variances of T_1 and T_2 in terms of p.

Hence state, with a reason, which is the better estimator. (6)

(c) Give **one** reason why the quality control manager should look at the

values of $\frac{X}{50}$ and $\frac{Y}{150}$. (1)

12. (A3 1998) In each trial of a random experiment, the probability of a success is a constant p. In n independent trials of the experiment, let X denote the number of successes obtained. Show that $\frac{X(X-1)}{n(n-1)}$ is an unbiased estimator for p^2. (4)

13. (S2 1999) An office uses balls of string to tie up parcels. When the string remaining on a ball is thought to be too short for further use, it is discarded. The length, X cm, of string on a discarded ball has a uniform distribution over the interval $(0,\theta)$ where θ is unknown.

(a) Write down the mean and the variance of X in terms of θ. (1)

(b) The length, x cm, of the string remaining on each of a random sample of 9 discarded balls was measured. The following results were calculated from the measured lengths:

$$\sum x = 108.9, \quad \sum x^2 = 1717.69.$$

Calculate an unbiased estimate of (i) θ, (ii) θ^2. (5)

14. (A3 1999) Two instruments are used to measure the concentration, μ, of a certain solution. Instrument 1 is such that the reading, X, obtained is a normally distributed random variable with mean μ and variance σ_x^2. Instrument 2 is such that the reading, Y, obtained ids a normally distributed random variable with mean μ and variance σ_y^2.

It is required to estimate μ using the statistic $T = \lambda X + (1 - \lambda)Y$, where λ is a constant.

(a) Show that T is an unbiased estimator of μ for all values of λ. (2)

(b) Obtain an expression for the variance of T in terms of λ, σ_x and σ_y. Hence showthat the value of λ which minimises the variance of T is

$$\lambda = \sigma_y^2/(\sigma_x^2 + \sigma_y^2). \tag{4}$$

Chapter 3

Interval estimation of a parameter

Introduction

In Chapter 2 an unknown population parameter was estimated by a single value (a point estimate) calculated from a random sample of observations. For an unbiased estimator we showed how its standard error was appropriate as a measure of its reliability in the sense that the smaller the standard error the more likely it was that the estimator would yield an estimate close to the true value of the parameter. However, knowing the standard error of an estimator does not by itself provide direct information on how close the estimate is to the true parameter value. This shortcoming led to the development of an interval estimate of a parameter, the interval being a range of values which, with a measurable degree of confidence, includes the true value of the parameter.

Let X_1, X_2, . . ., X_n denote a random sample of n observations of a random variable whose distribution involves a parameter θ whose value is not known. Here we shall assume that we can find a statistic $T \equiv T(X_1, X_2, . . ., X_n)$ which is an unbiased estimator of θ and whose sampling distribution is normal or approximately normal.

3.1 Interval estimation of the mean of a normal distribution whose variance is known

Let $\overline{X}$ denote the mean of a random sample of n observations of a random variable which is normally distributed with mean μ (unknown) and variance σ^2 (known). We know that the sampling distribution of $\overline{X}$ is normal with mean μ and standard error $\sigma/\sqrt{n}$.

Hence
$$Z = \frac{\overline{X} - \mu}{SE(\overline{X})} \sim N(0, 1). \tag{1}$$

Referring to Table 4 (RND or M&B) we find, for example, that
$$P(Z \geq 1.96) = P(Z \leq -1.96) = 0.025.$$

Combining these results we obtain (see Figure 3.1)
$$P(-1.96 \leq Z \leq 1.96) = 0.95. \tag{2}$$

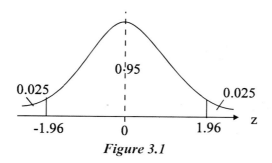

Figure 3.1

In particular, for Z defined by (1)

$$P\left(-1.96 \le \frac{\overline{X}-\mu}{SE(\overline{X})} \le 1.96\right) = 0.95,$$

or, equivalently, on rearranging the inequalities,

$$P[\overline{X} - 1.96\ SE(\overline{X}) \le \mu \le \overline{X} + 1.96\ SE(\overline{X})] = 0.95. \tag{3}$$

Reading (3) may suggest that it is a probabilistic statement about μ, but this cannot be so since μ is a constant not a random variable. The correct interpretation of (3) is that it is a probabilistic statement about the **random interval** $[\overline{X} - 1.96\ SE(\overline{X}), \overline{X} + 1.96\ SE(\overline{X})]$ in the sense that the probability that this interval will include the true value of μ is 0.95. This means that 95% of all possible random samples of size n will yield a value $\overline{x}$ of $\overline{X}$ such that the interval $[\overline{x} - 1.96\ SE(\overline{X}), \overline{x} + 1.96\ SE(\overline{X})]$ includes the true value of μ. Thus 5% of all such intervals will not include the true value of μ. Given $\overline{x}$, the interval

$$[\overline{x} - 1.96\ SE(\overline{X}), \overline{x} + 1.96\ SE(\overline{X})] \tag{4}$$

is called a 95% **confidence interval** for μ, and the endpoints of the interval are called the 95% **confidence limits** for μ. The method we have used to derive the interval (4) enables us to be 95% confident that the sample obtained is one of those for which (4) does include the true value of μ.

A confidence interval for any specified confidence level (95% above) can be obtained in a similar way. The confidence level to use in any situation is a matter of choice dependent upon the consequences of any erroneous decision from assuming that μ is in the interval when, in fact, it is not in the interval. The more serious the consequences the higher should be the chosen confidence level.

To generalise the above, let z_α be the value such that $P(Z \ge z_\alpha) = \alpha$, for some specified value of α between 0 and 0.5. Then (See Figure 3.2)

$$P(-z_\alpha \le Z \le z_\alpha) = 1 - 2\alpha.$$

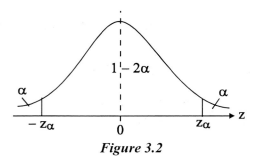

Figure 3.2

Replacing Z by $(\overline{X} - \mu)/SE(\overline{X})$ and rearranging the inequalities we have
$$P[\overline{X} - z_\alpha\, SE(\overline{X}) \le \mu \le \overline{X} + z_\alpha\, SE(\overline{X})] = 1 - 2\alpha,$$
from which it follows that $100(1 - 2\alpha)\%$ confidence limits for μ are
$$\overline{x} \pm z_\alpha\, SE(\overline{X}), \qquad\qquad (5)$$
where $\overline{x}$ is the observed sample mean and $SE(\overline{X}) = \sigma/\sqrt{n}$.

For example, to determine 90% confidence limits for μ we need the value of α such that $1 - 2\alpha = 0.9$; that is $\alpha = 0.05$. Referring to Table 4 (RND or M&B) we find $z_{0.05} = 1.645$ correct to three decimal places. Hence, 90% confidence limits for μ are given by
$$\overline{x} \pm 1.645\, SE(\overline{X}) \qquad\qquad (6)$$
It is evident that the narrower the confidence interval the more informative it is about the value of μ. From (5) the width of the $100(1 - 2\alpha)\%$ confidence interval is $2 \times z_\alpha \times SE(\overline{X})$. For a narrower interval we should decrease either z_α or $SE(\overline{X})$ or both. Decreasing z_α means increasing α and, therefore, decreasing $1 - 2\alpha$, which means decreasing the confidence level. Since $SE(\overline{X}) = \sigma/\sqrt{n}$, it may be decreased by increasing the sample size n, which means that the larger the sample size the better, in the sense that increasing the sample size reduces the width of the confidence interval for any given α.

Example 1

Repeated weighings of an object on a chemical balance give readings that are normally distributed with mean equal to the true weight of the object and standard deviation 0.5 mg.

(a) Given that 10 independent weighings of an object gave a mean reading of 12.3 mg, calculate 95% confidence limits for the true weight of the object.

(b) Find the least number of weighings of an object that are necessary for the width of the 95% confidence interval for the true weight of the object to be less than 0.5 mg.

Solution

(a)   Let the true weight of the object be μ mg. Then, the sample mean $\overline{X}$ mg of the readings of 10 weighings of the object will be normally distributed with mean μ and standard error $SE(\overline{X}) = 0.5/\sqrt{10}$. From (4) with $\overline{x} = 12.3$, 95% confidence limits for μ are

$$12.3 \pm 1.96 \times \frac{0.5}{\sqrt{10}} = 12.3 \pm 0.31 = 11.99 \text{ to } 12.61.$$

(b) From (4) we see that the width of the 95% confidence interval is

$$2 \times 1.96 \times SE(\overline{X}) = 3.92 \times 0.5/\sqrt{n} = 1.96/\sqrt{n}.$$

For this to be less than 0.5 we must have

$$\frac{1.96}{\sqrt{n}} < 0.5, \text{ or } n > \left(\frac{1.96}{0.5}\right)^2 = 15.37.$$

Hence, at least 16 weighings are necessary.

Exercise 3.1

1. In a random sample of 16 observations from the distribution $N(\mu, 9)$ the sum of the values obtained was 44. Calculate a 95% confidence interval for μ.

2. A random sample of 25 labourers had a mean weight of 75.8 kg. Assuming that the weights of labourers are normally distributed with standard deviation 9 kg, find 99% confidence limits for the mean weight of labourers.

3. From the results obtained in a random sample of n observations from a normal distribution having standard deviation 2, an investigator reported (0.73, 1.71) as the 95% confidence interval for the mean of the distribution. Deduce the value of n and the mean of the sample observations.

4. A random sample of 100 mass-produced washers had a mean thickness of 3.036 mm. Assuming that the thicknesses of such washers are normally distributed with standard deviation 0.2 mm, calculate 95% confidence limits for the mean thickness of such washers. Do your limits support the manufacturer's claim that the washers have a mean thickness of 3 mm?

5. The outcome X of a certain biological experiment is known to be normally distributed with standard deviation 5. A biologist wants to estimate the distribution mean by a 95% confidence interval of width less than 3. Determine the least number of experiments that the biologist should perform.

6. Items produced in a factory have masses which are normally distributed. The mean mass μ can be varied but the standard deviation is known to be 0.05 kg for all values of μ. A large batch of items is supposed to have a mean mass of exactly 3.5 kg. Twenty items were selected at random from the batch. Find a 99% confidence interval in each of the cases when the observed sample mean mass was (a) 3.45 kg, (b) 3.48 kg. For each of the

intervals you obtain state whether it is consistent with the claim that the mean mass of the items in the batch is 3.5 kg.

7. The random sample

$$2.982, \ 1.934, \ 4.028, \ 3.502, \ 0.732, \ 4.695, \ 3.082, \ 2.975, \ 5.204$$

was obtained from a $N(\mu, 1)$ distribution. Calculate a 95% confidence interval for μ.

8. In an experiment, 100 observations were taken from a normal distribution whose standard deviation is 4. The experimenter quoted (1.545, 2.861) as a confidence interval for the distribution mean. Determine the confidence level that was used.

9. The lifetimes of light bulbs of a particular brand are normally distributed with standard deviation 33 hours.

(a) A random sample of 9 light bulbs had a mean lifetime of 983 hours. Find a 90% confidence interval for the mean lifetime of bulbs of this brand.

(b) Find the least sample size such that a 99% confidence interval for the mean lifetime of these light bulbs has a width of less than 10 hours.

A further note on confidence intervals

Corresponding to any specified confidence level there are many confidence intervals for μ. In (4) above we showed that $[\overline{x} - 1.96 \ SE(\overline{X}), \ \overline{x} + 1.96 \ SE(\overline{X})]$ was a 95% confidence interval for μ. This interval was derived using the results

$$P(Z \leq -1.96) = P(Z \geq 1.96) = 0.025$$

with $Z = (\overline{X} - \mu)/SE(\overline{X})$, which has the distribution $N(0, 1)$. From Table 4, we find, for example, that

$$P(Z \leq -2.326) = 0.01 \ \text{ and } \ P(Z \geq 1.751) = 0.04,$$

which combined gives

$$P(-2.326 \leq Z \leq 1.751) = 0.95.$$

Replacing Z by $(\overline{X} - \mu)/SE(\overline{X})$ and rearranging the inequalities we have

$$P[\overline{X} - 1.751 \ SE(\overline{X}) \leq \mu \leq \overline{X} + 2.326 \ SE(\overline{X})] = 0.95,$$

from which it follows that the interval having the limits

$$\overline{x} - 1.751 \ SE(\overline{X}) \ \text{ and } \ \overline{x} + 2.326 \ SE(\overline{X}) \tag{7}$$

is also a 95% confidence interval for μ. Note that the width of this interval is equal to $4.077 \ SE(\overline{X})$, which is wider than the interval given in (4). It is easy to verify from a diagram that (4) is the shortest possible 95% confidence interval. In general, the interval given by (5) is the shortest $100(1 - 2\alpha)\%$ confidence interval for any given α. Henceforth, any reference to a confidence interval will mean the shortest one as given by (5). As an exercise find another 95% confidence interval for μ and verify that it is wider than the one given by (4).

3.2 Interval estimation of the difference between the means of two normal distributions whose variances are known

Consider the estimation of $\mu_1 - \mu_2$, where μ_1 and μ_2 are the means of two normal distributions having known variances σ_1^2 and σ_2^2, respectively. Let $\overline{X}_1$ denote the mean of a random sample of n_1 observations from $N(\mu_1, \sigma_1^2)$ and let $\overline{X}_2$ denote the mean of an independent random sample of n_2 observations from $N(\mu_2, \sigma_2^2)$. Then, the sampling distribution of $\overline{X}_1 - \overline{X}_2$ is normal with mean

$$E(\overline{X}_1 - \overline{X}_2) = \mu_1 - \mu_2 \tag{1}$$

and standard error

$$SE(\overline{X}_1 - \overline{X}_2) = \left(\frac{\sigma_1^2}{n_1} + \frac{\sigma_2^2}{n_2} \right)^{1/2}. \tag{2}$$

Proceeding as in Section 3.1 but replacing $\overline{X}$ by $(\overline{X}_1 - \overline{X}_2)$ and $SE(\overline{X})$ by $SE(\overline{X}_1 - \overline{X}_2)$ we find that the $100(1 - 2\alpha)\%$ confidence limits for $\mu_1 - \mu_2$ given the observed values $\overline{x}_1$ and $\overline{x}_2$ are

$$\overline{x}_1 - \overline{x}_2 \pm z_\alpha \, SE(\overline{X}_1 - \overline{X}_2) \tag{3}$$

Example

The mean lifetimes μ_A, μ_B of two types of light bulbs (A and B) were compared by testing 20 of type A and 25 of type B until failure. The sample mean for type A was 1021.3 hours and that for type B was 1005.7 hours. Assuming that for both types the lifetimes are normally distributed with standard deviation 30 hours, find a 95% confidence interval for the difference $\mu_A - \mu_B$ and comment on the result.

Solution

Denoting the sample means by $\overline{X}_A$ and $\overline{X}_B$ it follows from (2) above that

$$SE(\overline{X}_A - \overline{X}_B) = \sqrt{\frac{900}{20} + \frac{900}{25}} = 9.$$

Using (3) with $\alpha = 0.025$ the 95% confidence limits for $\mu_A - \mu_B$ are

$$(1021.3 - 1005.7) \pm 1.96 \times 9 = 15.6 \pm 17.64$$

so that the confidence interval is $(- 2.04, 33.24)$.

Comment. Since the confidence interval includes zero we cannot, with 95% confidence, conclude that the means are different. However, the bulk of the interval contains positive values which suggests it may be worthwhile increasing the sample sizes (which will reduce the standard error) thereby possibly having an interval of positive values from which one could then conclude with 95% confidence that $\mu_A > \mu_B$. Alternatively, if we are prepared to lower our level of confidence to 90% then the 90% confidence interval (replacing 1.96 by 1.645) is $(0.795, 30.405)$, in which case with 90% confidence we could conclude that $\mu_A > \mu_B$. [A more formal treatment of the type of problem discussed here will be given in the next chapter.]

Exercise 3.2

1. A random sample of 9 observations from a normal distribution having standard deviation 4 had a mean of 122. A random sample of 16 observations from another normal distribution having standard deviation 5 had a mean of 101. Calculate a 99% confidence interval for the difference between the means of the two distributions.

2. A random sample of 25 observations from a normal distribution having standard deviation 5 has a mean of 80. A random sample of 36 observations from another normal distribution having standard deviation 3 had a mean of 75. Calculate 98% confidence limits for the difference between the means of the two distributions.

3. Repeated weighings of an object on a chemical balance give readings that are normally distributed with mean equal to the true weight of the object and standard deviation 0.5 mg. Ten weighings of an object A gave a mean reading of 8.6 mg, while fifteen readings of an object B gave a mean reading of 6.8 mg. Calculate a 90% confidence interval for the difference between the true weights of A and B.

4. The quality of a mass-produced item is measured on a continuous scale and experience has shown that the qualities are normally distributed with a variance of 4.72. It is also known that any minor modification to the process will affect only the mean quality of the items. A random sample of 25 items produced under one modification had a mean quality of 26.4, while a random sample of 20 items under another type of modification had a mean quality of 25.6. Calculate a 95% confidence interval for the difference between the mean qualities under the two types of modification. Does the result suggest that one of the modifications will lead to better quality items on the average?

5. In an investigation of the effect of an additive on the viscosity of an oil, the mean of five independent measurements of its viscosity without the additive was 6.87, whereas the mean of six independent measurements of its viscosity with the additive was 7.41. Assuming that in both cases the measurements are normally distributed with mean equal to the true value and standard deviation 0.5, find (a) a 90% confidence interval, (b) a 99% confidence interval, for the difference in viscosities with and without the additive. Comment on your results.

6. The random variables X and Y are independent and have normal distributions with unknown means μ and λ, and common variance 32.84. A 90% confidence interval is required for the difference $\mu - \lambda$ and is to be calculated from the results of independent random samples of n observations of X and n observations of Y. Find the smallest n for the width of the interval to be less than 4.

3.3 Approximate confidence limits

The confidence limits considered so far are applicable only when the distributions being sampled are normal. In this section we consider some particular cases where it is possible to calculate approximate confidence limits for a parameter θ of a non-normal distribution. Essentially, our method will assume that we can find an unbiased estimator of θ whose sampling distribution is approximately normal.

3.3.1 Large-sample approximate confidence limits for a population mean

Let $\overline{X}$ denote the mean of a random sample of n observations from a distribution having mean μ and variance σ^2. Provided that n is large, it follows from the Central Limit Theorem (Section 1.3.2) that the sampling distribution of $\overline{X}$ is approximately normal with mean μ and standard error $SE(\overline{X}) = \sigma/\sqrt{n}$. Using this approximation, it follows from (5) of Section 3.1 that if $\overline{x}$ is the observed value of $\overline{X}$ then the interval having the limits

$$\overline{x} \pm z_\alpha \, SE(\overline{X}) \tag{1}$$

is an approximate $100(1 - 2\alpha)\%$ confidence interval for μ.

Since $SE(\overline{X})$ involves σ, the above can be used to calculate an approximate confidence interval for μ only if the value of σ is known. When σ is unknown we can introduce a further approximation by replacing σ^2 by its sample unbiased estimate s^2 given by (3) in Section 2.3. For large n, it is reasonable to expect that s^2 will not be very different from σ^2. In this case the approximate $100(1 - 2\alpha)\%$ confidence limits for μ are

$$\overline{x} \pm z_\alpha \, ESE(\overline{X}) \tag{2}$$

where

$$ESE(\overline{X}) = \sqrt{(s^2/n)} = \sqrt{[(\Sigma x^2 - n\overline{x}^2)/n(n - 1)]} \tag{3}$$

The larger the value of n, the closer will be the limits given by (3) to the actual $100(1 - 2\alpha)\%$ confidence limits for μ.

Example

A random sample of 100 observations of a random variable X had values whose sum was 185.6 and whose sum of squares was 385.89. Calculate approximate 90% confidence limits for the mean, μ, of X. Deduce approximate 90% confidence limits for $3\mu - 2$.

Solution

Letting x denote an arbitrary sample observation we are given that

$$\Sigma x = 185.6 \quad \text{and} \quad \Sigma x^2 = 385.89.$$

Hence, the unbiased estimates of the population mean and variance are, respectively,

$$\overline{x} = 185.6/100 = 1.856,$$

and
$$s^2 = \frac{1}{99}[385.89 - 100 \times 1.856^2] \cong 0.4183.$$

It follows that
$$\mathrm{ESE}(\overline{X}) = \sqrt{\frac{s^2}{100}} \cong \sqrt{0.004183} \cong 0.0647$$

Using (2) above with $\alpha = 0.05$, approximate 90% confidence limits for μ are
$$1.856 \pm 1.645 \times 0.0647 = 1.856 \pm 0.106 = (1.750, 1.962).$$
The corresponding approximate 90% confidence limits for $3\mu - 2$ are :
$$3 \times 1.750 - 2 = 3.250 \quad \text{and} \quad 3 \times 1.962 - 2 = 3.886$$

Exercise 3.3a

1. The breaking strengths, x kg, of a random sample of 60 lengths of string were such that $\Sigma x = 435.6$ and $\Sigma x^2 = 3204.7$. Calculate unbiased estimates of the mean and the variance of the breaking strengths of such strings. Hence find approximate 95% confidence limits for the mean breaking strength of such lengths of string.

2. A random sample of 100 observations from a population gave unbiased estimates of the population mean and variance equal to 15.8 and 5.6842, respectively. Find an approximate 99% confidence interval for the population mean μ. Deduce approximate 99% confidence limits for $(\mu - 2)/2$.

3. The heights of a random sample of 80 male students were measured in metres. It was found that the sum of the 80 heights was 140.8 and the sum of their squares was 248.64. Calculate an approximate 90% confidence interval for the mean height of male students.

4. The masses, x grams, of the contents of 100 jars of jam were such that $\Sigma x = 45426$ and $\Sigma x^2 = 20635238$. Calculate unbiased estimates of the mean and the variance of the masses of jam in such jars. Hence find an approximate 90% confidence interval for the mean mass per jar.

5. The yields, x kg, from a random sample of 100 tomato plants were such that $\Sigma x = 700$ and $\Sigma x^2 = 5296$. Calculate unbiased estimates of the mean and the variance of the yields from such plants. Hence find an approximate 98% confidence interval for the mean yield per plant. The tomatoes are sold for 75 pence per kg. Assuming that the cost per plant to the grower is 25 pence, find approximate 98% confidence limits for the grower's mean profit per plant.

6. A random sample of 80 electrical elements produced by a certain company had resistances, x ohms, such that $\Sigma x = 790$ and $\Sigma x^2 = 7821$. Find approximate 95% confidence limits for the mean resistance for electrical elements produced by the company.

7. The lifetimes, x hours, of a random sample of 260 electronic components were such that $\Sigma x = 3952$ and $\Sigma x^2 = 62320$. Determine an approximate 95% confidence interval for the mean lifetime of such components.

8. The following table shows the frequency distribution of the number (x) of days that a random sample of 120 pupils at a school had been absent during the previous term.

Number of days absent (x)	0	1	2	3	4	5
Number of pupils	48	25	20	18	5	4

Find an approximate 95% confidence interval for the mean number of days that a pupil at this school was absent during the previous term.

3.3.2 Large-sample approximate confidence limits for the difference between the means of two populations

Let $\overline{X}_1$ denote the mean of a random sample of n_1 observations from a population having mean μ_1 and variance σ_1^2, and let $\overline{X}_2$ denote the mean of an independent random sample of n_2 observations from a population having mean μ_2 and variance σ_2^2. Then, as in Section 3.2, the sampling distribution of $\overline{X}_1 - \overline{X}_2$ has

$$\text{mean} \quad E(\overline{X}_1 - \overline{X}_2) = \mu_1 - \mu_2 \tag{1}$$

$$\text{and standard error} \quad SE(\overline{X}_1 - \overline{X}_2) = \sqrt{\frac{\sigma_1^2}{n_1} + \frac{\sigma_2^2}{n_2}} \tag{2}$$

Furthermore, provided n_1 and n_2 are large, the sampling distribution of $\overline{X}_1 - \overline{X}_2$ will be approximately normal with mean given by (1) and standard deviation given by (2). Also, if σ_1 and σ_2 are unknown, then for large n_1 and n_2, (2) may be approximated by

$$ESE(\overline{X}_1 - \overline{X}_2) = \sqrt{\frac{s_1^2}{n_1} + \frac{s_2^2}{n_2}} \tag{3}$$

where s_1^2 and s_2^2 are the sample unbiased estimates of σ_1^2 and σ_2^2, respectively.
It follows that for large n_1 and n_2 approximate $100(1 - 2\alpha)\%$ confidence limits for $\mu_1 - \mu_2$ are given by

$$(\overline{x}_1 - \overline{x}_2) \pm z_\alpha \, ESE(\overline{X}_1 - \overline{X}_2) \tag{4}$$

where $\overline{x}_1$ and $\overline{x}_2$ are the observed values of $\overline{X}_1$ and $\overline{X}_2$, respectively.

Example

The lifetimes in hours of a random sample of 80 electric light bulbs of brand A gave unbiased estimates of the population mean and variance equal to 1070 and 472, respectively. The lifetimes in hours of a random sample of 60 electric light bulbs of brand B gave unbiased estimates of the population mean and variance equal to 1042 and 366, respectively. Calculate an approximate 90% confidence interval for the difference between the mean lifetimes of the two brands of electric bulbs.

Solution

From the given information and using subscript A for brand A bulbs and subscript B for brand B bulbs, we have

$$n_A = 80, \ \bar{x}_A = 1070, \ s_A^2 = 472 \ ; \ n_B = 60, \ \bar{x}_B = 1042, \ s_B^2 = 366.$$

Hence, from (3), the estimate of $SE(\bar{X}_A - \bar{X}_B)$ is

$$ESE \ (\bar{X}_A - \bar{X}_B) = \sqrt{\frac{s_A^2}{n_A} + \frac{s_B^2}{n_B}} = \sqrt{\frac{472}{80} + \frac{366}{60}} = \sqrt{12}$$

For the 90% confidence interval we need $\alpha = 0.05$; from Table 4, we find that $z_{0.05} = 1.645$.

Using (4) above the approximate 90% confidence limits for $\mu_A - \mu_B$ are

$$(1070 - 1042) \pm 1.645\sqrt{12} = 28 \pm 5.70$$

so that the approximate 90% confidence interval is (22.3, 33.7).

Thus with 90% confidence we can say that, on average, a brand A bulb will last between 22 hours and 34 hours longer than a brand B bulb.

Exercise 3.3b

1. In an investigation to determine the amounts spent on sweets per week by boys and girls in a particular age-group, a survey was conducted on random samples of 80 boys and 70 girls. The results of the survey gave unbiased estimates of the mean and the variance of the amounts spent in pence per week by boys equal to 96 and 9.8 respectively, and by girls equal to 89 and 12.4, respectively. Calculate approximate 99% confidence limits for the difference between the average amounts spent per week on sweets by boys and girls. Comment on the interval you obtain.

2. The following table summarises the results obtained in an experiment designed to compare the heights of stalks of wheat under two fertiliser treatments A and B.

	Fertiliser A	Fertiliser B
Number of stalks	50	60
Sum of heights	780	846
Sum of squares of heights	12358	12195

Find an approximate 90% confidence interval for the difference between the mean heights of stalks of wheat grown under the two fertiliser treatments.

3. A group of 150 patients was divided into two equal subgroups A and B. Patients in A were given a tranquilliser of one type while those in B were given a tranquilliser of a different type. The observed numbers of hours of sleep by the patients in A gave unbiased estimates of the population mean and variance equal to 7.25 and 0.7225, while the corresponding figures for B were 7.45 and 0.49. Find an approximate 90% confidence interval for the difference in the mean hours of sleep produced by the two types of tranquilliser.

4. The heights, measured in metres, of a random sample of 200 women had a sum of 316.00 and the sum of their squares was 499.9964. Calculate an approximate 95% confidence interval for the mean height of the women.

The heights, measured in metres, of a random sample of 150 men had a sum of 258.12 and the sum of their squares was 444.5454. Calculate an approximate 99% confidence interval for the difference between the mean heights of men and women.

5. The amounts, x millilitres, of a liquid dispensed by machine A into 300 phials were such that $\Sigma x = 39600$ and $\Sigma x^2 = 5231984$. Calculate unbiased estimates of the mean μ_A and the variance σ_A^2 of the amounts dispensed per phial by machine A. Determine an approximate 90% confidence interval for μ_A.

The amounts, y millilitres, of a liquid dispensed by machine B into 400 phials gave unbiased estimates of 135 and 36 for the mean μ_B and the variance σ_B^2 of the amounts dispensed per phial by machine B. Find an approximate 90% confidence interval for $\mu_A - \mu_B$.

6. A random sample of 200 fibres was drawn from a large bundle of fibres. The breaking strength x of each fibre was measured and it was found that $\Sigma x = 3580.0$ and $\Sigma x^2 = 64529.75$. Find an approximate 95% confidence interval for the mean breaking strength μ of the fibres in the bundle.

After the remaining fibres in the bundle had been treated with a certain chemical, a second random sample of 200 fibres was taken. The breaking strengths of these fibres gave unbiased estimates of the mean λ an the variance of the fibres in the bundle equal to 18.1 and 0.99, respectively. Find an approximate 95% confidence interval for $\mu - \lambda$. Comment on whether your interval suggests that the chemical treatment has altered the mean breaking strength of the fibres.

7. An experiment was conducted to compare two slimming diets A and B. Two groups, each of 50 overweight people, were selected randomly. One group followed diet A while the other followed diet B for a period of 20 weeks. A summary of the weight losses achieved are given in the following table.

	Diet A	Diet B
Sum of weight losses	965	680
Sum of squares of weight losses	18956	9425

Find an approximate 95% confidence interval for the difference in the mean weight losses for the two diets. Interpret your answer.

8. A process extracts two chemicals A and B from 1 kg batches of raw material. The amount of A extracted from a batch is X grams, where X is a continuous random variable having mean μ and standard deviation 2, and the amount of B extracted is Y grams, where Y is a continuous random variable having mean λ and standard deviation 3. It may be assumed that X and Y are independent. Chemical A is valued at £2 per gram, while chemical B is valued at £1 per gram. The process was applied to 100 batches, the means of the amounts of A and B extracted per batch being 5.2 grams and 8.6 grams, respectively. Calculate approximate 95% confidence limits for the mean total value of the chemicals extracted per batch. [HINT: you will need to consider the sampling distribution $2\overline{X} + \overline{Y}$.]

3.3.3 Approximate confidence limits for a probability

Let X denote the number of successes in n independent Bernoulli trials in each of which the probability of a success is θ (unknown). As indicated in Section 1.4 the sampling distribution of $P = X/n$, the proportion of successes in the n trials, is such that

$$E(P) = \theta \text{ and } SE(P) = \sqrt{[\theta(1 - \theta)/n]}.$$

For large n and θ not close to 0 or 1, the sampling distribution of P is approximately normal with the above mean and standard error. Hence, proceeding as in the preceding sections, approximate $100(1 - 2\alpha)\%$ confidence limits for θ are

$$p \pm z_\alpha SE(P),$$

where p is the observed value of P. However, these limits cannot be evaluated because SE(P) depends on θ whose value is unknown. As in Section 2.2 we can estimate SE(P) by using

$$ESE(P) = \sqrt{[p(1 - p)/n]}.$$

Using this estimate, approximate $100(1 - 2\alpha)\%$ confidence limits for θ are

$$p \pm z_\alpha ESE(P),$$

whose values can be evaluated given the observed sample proportion p of successes.

[In the above we used two approximations, namely, the normal approximation to the sampling distribution of P and ESE(P) as an approximation to SE(P). A method exists whereby the second of these approximations is not necessary (see Question 11 of the following exercise). The method is quite complicated and is rarely used since the limits given above are sufficiently accurate for most practical purposes.]

Example 1

In a random sample of 400 male voters from a very large electoral region it was found that 140 of them stated that they intended to vote for candidate A in the forthcoming election. Calculate approximate 95% confidence limits for the proportion of all male voters in the electorate who intend to vote for candidate A.

Solution

Here, $n = 400$ is large and $p = 140/400 = 0.35$ is not close to 0 or 1, so that the conditions for the above to apply are satisfied. We have

$$ESE(P) = \sqrt{[0.35 \times 0.65/400]}.$$

For the 95% confidence limits, α must be such that $1 - 2\alpha = 0.95$ so that $\alpha = 0.025$ and form Table 4 we find that $z_{0.025} = 1.960$. It follows that the approximate 95% confidence limits of the proportion of all male voters intending to vote for candidate A are

$$0.35 \pm 1.960 \times \sqrt{[0.35 \times 0.65/400]} = 0.35 \pm 0.047 = 0.303 \text{ and } 0.397.$$

Thus, with approximately 95% confidence, we can say that between 30% and 40% of all male voters intend to vote for candidate A.

Example 2

A random sample of 500 fish was taken from a lake, marked, and returned to the lake. Some time later a second random sample of 200 fish was taken and was found to include 25 marked fish. (a) Estimate the number N of fish in the lake. (b) Calculate approximate 90% confidence limits for the proportion θ of marked fish in the lake. (c) Deduce approximate 90% confidence limits for N.

Solution

(a) An estimate of θ is $p = 25/200 = 0.125$ and the corresponding estimate of N is

$$500/p = 4000.$$

(b) Now $ESE(P) = \sqrt{[p(1 - p)/n]} = \sqrt{[0.125 \times 0.875/200]} \cong 0.023385$

Hence, approximate 90% confidence limits for θ are

$$0.125 \pm 1.645 \times 0.023385 \cong 0.125 \pm 0.038 = 0.087 \text{ and } 0.163$$

(c) Since our estimator of N is $500/P$, the corresponding limits for N, correct to the nearest integer, are

$$500/0.087 = 5747 \text{ and } 500/0.163 = 3067.$$

Thus, with approximately 90% confidence, we can say that the number of fish in the lake lies between 3067 and 5747.

Exercise 3.3c

1. In a random sample of 1000 households in a large city it was found that 358 had two or more cars. Calculate approximate 90% confidence limits for the proportion of all households in the city that have two or more cars.

2. In a random sample of 500 births registered during a certain month it was found that 261 were boys. Calculate approximate 95% confidence limits for the proportion of all registered births that are boys.

3. Sweets of assorted colours are sold in tubes, each tube containing 20 sweets. Of the sweets in a random sample of 40 such tubes it was found that 268 were black. Calculate approximate 96% confidence limits for the proportion of all sweets produced that are black.

4. An opinion poll revealed that 750 of a random sample of 1800 citizens were in favour of a proposal to build a new concert hall. Calculate an approximate 99% confidence interval for the proportion of citizens who support the proposal.

5. At the end of a severe winter an insurance company found that of 972 policy holders living in a certain county who had insured their homes with the company, 357 had suffered more than £500 worth of snow and frost damage. Calculate approximate 95% confidence limits for the proportion of all homeowners in the county who suffered more than £500 worth of damage from snow and frost.

6. A supermarket manager wishes to find a 95% confidence interval for the proportion θ of its customers who pay by cash. In a poll of 200 customers it was found that 40 paid by cash. (a) Calculate an approximate 95% confidence interval for θ. (b) Find the smallest number of customers that should be polled to ensure that the width of the 95% confidence interval for θ will be less than 0.1.

7. From the 2500 pupils at a school a random sample of 50 was chosen and it was found that 15 of them were left-handed. Find approximate 90% confidence limits for (a) the proportion of pupils in the school who are left-handed, (b) the number of pupils in the school who are left-handed.

8. A random sample of 400 rabbits in a particular area was caught, tagged and released in the same area. Later, a second random sample of 360 rabbits was caught and of these 18 were found to be tagged. (a) Estimate the number N of rabbits in the area. (b) Find approximate 95% confidence limits for N.

9. In a random sample of 200 resistors of a particular brand it was found that 13 of them failed to meet the specified tolerance. Denoting by θ the proportion of all such resistors that fail to meet the specified tolerance, write down an unbiased estimate of θ and obtain an estimate of its standard error. Hence calculate an approximate 95% confidence interval for the value of θ. State whether or not your result supports the manufacturer's claim that $\theta = 0.04$.

10. In a random sample of 100 observations of a continuous random variable it was found that 64 of them had values greater than 3. Use this information to obtain an unbiased estimate of $\theta = P(X > 3)$, and find an estimate of its standard error. Hence find approximate 95% confidence limits for θ, giving each limit correct to two decimal places. Given, further, that X has the uniform distribution over the interval from $\beta - 1$ to $\beta + 1$, where β is an unknown constant, obtain an expression for θ in terms of β. Hence find approximate 95% confidence limits for β giving each limit correct to two decimal places.

11. In observations of a particular type of event, the probability of a positive result of any one observation is independent of the results of other observations and has the value θ, the same for all observations. In n observations the proportion giving positive results is P. Using a normal approximation to the sampling distribution of P show that

$$P(\,|\,P - \theta\,| < 1.96\ \sqrt{[\theta(1 - \theta)/n]}) \approx 0.95.$$

In a set of 100 observations of this type, 90 gave a positive result. Obtain an inequality of the above form, and by squaring both sides of the inequality calculate from the roots of a quadratic equation an approximate 95% confidence interval for the value of θ.

3.3.4 Approximate confidence limits for the mean of a Poisson distribution.

Let $\overline{X}$ denote the mean of a large random sample of n observations of a Poisson random variable whose mean μ is unknown. Since the variance of this Poisson distribution is also μ it follows from the Central Limit Theorem that the sampling distribution of $\overline{X}$ may be approximated by a normal distribution having mean $E(\overline{X}) = \mu$ and standard error $SE(\overline{X}) = \sqrt{\mu / n}$.

Hence, approximate $100(1 - 2\alpha)\%$ confidence limits for μ are

$$\overline{x} \pm z_{\alpha} SE(\overline{X}),$$

where $\overline{x}$ is the observed sample mean. However, these limits cannot be evaluated since $SE(\overline{X})$ involves the unknown μ. To enable us to evaluate approximate confidence limits we can replace $SE(\overline{X})$ by its estimate $ESE(\overline{X}) = \sqrt{\overline{x} / n}$. We thus have the following approximate $100(1 - 2\alpha)\%$ confidence limits for μ:

$$\overline{x} \pm z_{\alpha} ESE(\overline{X}).$$

[More accurate limits can be obtained using a procedure similar to that for a probability outlined in Question 11 of Exercise 3.3.3, but the approximation given above should be of sufficient accuracy in practice].

Example

The number of cars that become overheated on any day along a stretch of motorway may be assumed to have a Poisson distribution. In a random sample of 50 days the total number of cars that became overheated was found to be 163. Calculate an approximate 95% confidence interval for the mean number of cars per day that become overheated.

Solution

Here n = 50 and $\bar{x}$ = 163/50 = 3.26. Hence ESE($\bar{X}$) = $\sqrt{3.26}/50$ and approximate 95% confidence limits for the mean μ are

$$\bar{x} \pm 1.96 \times ESE(\bar{X}) = 3.26 \pm 1.96 \times \sqrt{3.26}/50 = 3.26 \pm 0.500,$$

and the approximate 95% confidence interval for μ is (2.76, 3.76).

Exercise 3.3d

1. A total of 252 flaws were found in a random sample of 100 rolls of cloth. Calculate approximate 90% confidence limits for the mean number of flaws per roll.

2. Inspection of a random sample of 200 new cars of a particular model revealed a total of 135 defects. Assuming that the number of defects per car has a Poisson distribution determine approximate 95% confidence limits for the mean number of defects per new car.

3. The following table shows the observed frequency distribution of the numbers of bubbles found in a random sample of 60 glass bottles.

Number of bubbles per bottle	0	1	2	3
Number of bottles	28	19	8	5

Assuming that the number of bubbles per bottle has a Poisson distribution calculate approximate 92% confidence limits for the mean number of bubbles per bottle.

4. The number of emissions per minute from a radioactive source has a Poisson distribution with unknown mean μ. Given that a total of 5000 emissions occurred over a period of one hour calculate an approximate 95% confidence interval for μ.

5. The number of claims per week made on life insurance policies of a certain company has a Poisson distribution with mean μ. Given that 728 claims were made in the previous year calculate approximate 95% confidence limits for μ.

6. The number of blemished tomatoes on a plant may be assumed to have a Poisson distribution. Given that a total of 810 blemished tomatoes were found in a sample of 100 plants find the approximate 99% confidence limits for the mean number of blemished tomatoes per plant.

7. The number of cars arriving at a road junction in a period of 5 minutes may be assumed to have a Poisson distribution. The following table shows the frequency distribution of the number of cars arriving at the junction over 45 consecutive periods of 5 minutes each.

Number of cars	0	1	2	3	4	5
Number of periods	6	13	11	8	4	3

Calculate approximate 95% confidence limits for the mean number of cars arriving at the junction in a period of 5 minutes.

8. Suppose that X has the Poisson distribution with mean μ (unknown). A random sample of 100 observations of X had mean 6.1. Obtain an approximate 90% confidence interval for μ. Find also an approximate 90% confidence interval for $P(X = 0) = e^{-\mu}$.

Miscellaneous Questions on Chapter 3

1. (1984) The random variable X has probability density function f, where

$$f(x) = 1, \quad \text{for } \theta + 1 \leq x \leq \theta + 2,$$
$$f(x) = 0, \quad \text{otherwise,}$$

where θ is an unknown constant. Denoting the mean and the variance of X by μ and σ^2, respectively, express μ in terms of θ and find the value of σ^2. (4)

A random sample of 10 observations of X had the values :

$$2.4, \ 1.6, \ 1.7, \ 2.3, \ 1.9, \ 1.8, \ 1.6, \ 2.1, \ 1.6, \ 2.0$$

Calculate an unbiased estimate of μ, and deduce an unbiased estimate of θ. Calculate, to three significant figures, the standard error of your unbiased estimate of θ. (5)

Given that a random sample of 100 observations of X had mean 1.86, use a normal distribution approximation to calculate 95% confidence limits for θ, giving each limit correct to three significant figures. (6)

2. (1987) The random variable X is normally distributed with unknown mean μ cm and standard deviation 2 cm.

(i) A random sample of 16 observations of X had values which summed to 118.4 cm. Calculate a 95% confidence interval for the value of μ.

(ii) Find the smallest possible sample size of observations of X that should be taken for the width of the 95% confidence interval for μ to be less than 1 cm.　　(6)

3. (1987) The weekly wages received by a random sample of 80 personnel employed in factory A had a mean of £86.40 and a standard deviation of £3.80. Use this information to calculate an approximate 95% confidence interval for the mean weekly wage of all personnel employed in factory A.　　(4)

The weekly wages received by a random sample of 100 personnel employed in factory B had a mean of £87.60 and a standard deviation of £5.20. Calculate an approximate 95% confidence interval for the difference between the mean weekly wages in the two factories. State, with your reason, whether or not your interval discredits the claim that the mean weekly wages in the two factories are equal.　　(4)

4. (1988) When an object is weighed repeatedly using a certain balance the observed masses are normally distributed with mean equal to the true mass of the object and standard deviation 0.5 mg.

(a) Find the least number of times that an object should be weighed for the width of the 90% confidence interval for the object's true mass to be less than 0.5 mg.　　(3)

(b) An object was weighed 10 times on the balance and the mean of the observed masses was 6.8 mg. Another object was weighed 15 times on the balance and the mean of the observed masses was 4.6 mg. Calculate 95% confidence limits for the difference between the true masses of the two objects.　　(4)

5. (1991) The times taken by 125 workers using method A to complete a particular task had mean 30.2 minutes and standard deviation 2.2 minutes. The times taken by 100 workers using method B had mean 29.8 minutes and standard deviation 2.9 minutes. Calculate approximate 95% confidence limits for the difference between the mean times of the two methods to complete the task. State, with your reason, whether or not you would conclude that one method is faster, on average, than the other method.　　(4)

It is required to find a 95% confidence interval for the difference between the mean times of the two methods having a width of less than 1 minute. If n workers are assigned to method A and another n workers to method B, find the smallest value of n to meet the requirement. Assume that the times taken are normally distributed and that the sample standard deviations given above are the true population values.　　(5)

6. (1992) Mass produced ball bearings have diameters that are normally distributed with mean μ mm and standard deviation 0.03 mm. A random sample of 9 bearings had the following diameters (in mm) :

$$5.01,\ 5.03,\ 4.96,\ 4.91,\ 4.96,\ 5.06,\ 5.02,\ 4.94,\ 4.93$$

Calculate 95% confidence limits for μ.　　(3)

7. (1992) A choconut is a sweet consisting of a nut coated with chocolate, where the nut may be an almond or a cashew. Let the proportion of choconuts having an almond nut centre be θ. In a random sample of 100 choconuts it was found that 70 of them had almond centres. Write down an unbiased estimate, p, of θ and calculate an estimate of the standard error of p. Assuming that the sampling distribution of p is approximately normal, calculate 95% confidence limits for θ. (5)

8. (1994) When the alcohol level μ (in mg/100ml) of a specimen of blood is measured, the reading obtained is a normally distributed random variable with mean μ and standard deviation 2.

(a) 6 measurements of the alcohol level of a specimen were as follows:

$$70.3, \ 72.9, \ 69.6, \ 70.8, \ 67.2, \ 72.5.$$

Calculate 95% confidence limits for the value of μ for this specimen. (4)

(b) 6 measurements of the alcohol level of a second specimen were made. The sample mean was 72.9. Calculate 95% confidence limits for the difference between the alcohol levels of the two specimens. (4)

(c) A technician believes that these two specimens actually come from the same source. Comment briefly on this belief. (1)

9. (1995) The following seven observations were made on a random variable X that is normally distributed with unknown mean μ and standard deviation 0.3.

$$14.3, \ 15.1, \ 14.9, \ 14.8, \ 14.4, \ 14.9, \ 14.5$$

Calculate 99% confidence limits for μ. (4)

10. (1995) The birthweight (x kg) of each baby in random samples of babies born in two different countries was measured and the following results calculated.

Country A : sample size = 100; $\Sigma x = 340.2$; $\Sigma x^2 = 1238.42$

Country B : sample size = 120; $\Sigma x = 335.7$; $\Sigma x^2 = 1015.75$.

Calculate approximate confidence limits for the difference between the mean birthweights of babies born in the two countries. (7)

11. (1996) In a survey carried out among first year students at a large university, 242 students out of a random sample of 400 students expressed satisfaction with the facilities provided by the Students' Union. Calculate approximate 95% confidence limits for the proportion of first year students satisfied with the facilities provided by the Students' Union. (4)

12. (1996) A food manufacturer produces a large number of tins of sardines, with contents having a stated mean weight of 80 g. The weight, x g, of the contents of each of a random sample of 121 tins of sardines was measured and the following results calculated :

$$\Sigma x = 9716.3 \; ; \; \Sigma x^2 = 780346.09$$

(a) Calculate an unbiased estimate of the variance of the weights of the contents of tins produced by the manufacturer. (2)

(b)(i) Calculate approximate 90% confidence limits for the mean weight of the contents of tins produced by the manufacturer. (3)

(ii) State, with a reason, whether it was necessary to assume that the weights of the contents of tins were normally distributed. (1)

(c) State, with a reason, whether or not your results are consistent with the stated mean weight of 80 g. (1)

13. (A3 1997) A scientist measures the pH value of a solution using a certain instrument. The reading that she obtains can be assumed to be a normally distributed random variable with mean equal to the true pH value and standard deviation 0.12. She makes five measurements on a certain solution and obtains the following results.

$$6.22, 6.48, 6.36, 6.41, 6.30$$

Calculate a 95% confidence interval for the true pH value of the solution. (4)

14. (S2 1997) Let θ denote the probability that a new treatment will cure a patient suffering from a particular ailment. The treatment was administered to a random sample of 100 patients and it cured 80 of them.

(a) Write down an unbiased estimate of θ. (1)

(b) Calculate an estimate of the standard error of your answer to (a). (2)

(c) hence find approximate 90% confidence limits for θ. (2)

15. (A3 1998) The time, x seconds, taken by each of a random sample of 150 thirteen-year girls to run 400 m was recorded and the following results were obtained.

$$\sum x = 1038.0 , \quad \sum x^2 = 722481.44$$

It may be assumed that the times taken by thirteen-year old girls to run 400 m are normally distributed with mean μ seconds and standard deviation σ seconds.

(a) Calculate an unbiased estimate of σ^2. (2)

(b) Calculate an approximate 95% confidence interval for μ. (3)

(c) A sports scientist suggested beforehand that the value of μ was 68.5. State, giving a reason, whether or not these results support this suggestion. (1)

16. (S2 1998) The lengths, in metres, of cloth in rolls produced by a certain manufacturer are normally distributed with mean μ and standard deviation 0.08. The lengths, in metres, of a random sample of 5 rolls were:

50.09, 49.96, 49.92, 50.12, 50.01

(a) Calculate a 95% confidence interval for μ. (4)

17. (A3 1999) Random samples of male dogs and female dogs of a particular breed were selected. Each dog was weighed (in kilograms) and the following results were obtained.

Male dogs: Sample size = 100, mean = 20.84, variance = 4.36

Female dogs: Sample size = 80, mean = 19.61, variance = 3.92

(a) Calculate approximate 90% confidence limits for the difference in the mean weights of male and female dogs of this breed. (4)

(b) Give a reason why it was not necessary to assume that the weights were normally distributed. (1)

18. (S2 1999) In a large-scale experiment for comparing two diets A and B, 100 persons followed diet A and 80 followed diet B for one month. From the observed weight losses, unbiased estimates of the mean and the variance of the weight losses of persons following diet A for a month were calculated to be 2.97 kg and 1.62 kg^2, respectively. The corresponding estimates for persons following diet B for a month were 2.31 kg and 1.55 kg^2.

(a) Calculate an approximate 99% confidence interval for the difference between the mean weight losses for the two diets. State two assumptions that you have made. (7)

(b) State, with a reason, which of the two diets you would recommend. (1)

Chapter 4

Hypothesis Testing 2

Introduction

In this chapter we extend the procedure of hypothesis testing introduced in Chapter 3 of the S2 book to the testing of (i) a specified value for the mean of distribution (not necessarily normal) given a large sample and (ii) a specified difference between the means of two distributions. It will be assumed that you are familiar with the following terminology introduced earlier:

null and alternative hypotheses, test statistic, critical region, p-value, and significance level.

4.1   p-value

4.1.1 Approximate p-value when testing the mean of a distribution

Let X denote a random variable whose distribution is not known. Denote its mean by μ and its variance by σ^2. A random sample of n observations of X is to be used to test the null hypothesis H_0: $\mu = \mu_0$. We shall assume that n is large enough to justify using the Central Limit Theorem (Section 1.3.2). As we did in Section 3.3.1 we can approximate the sampling distribution of the sample mean $\overline{X}$ by the normal distribution having mean μ and variance σ^2/n. Thus, on assuming that H_0 is true

$$\overline{X} \approx N(\mu_0, \sigma^2/n)$$

If σ is not known then, as we did in Section 3.3.1, we can introduce the further approximation by replacing σ^2 by its unbiased estimate s^2, so that

$$\overline{X} \approx N(\mu_0, s^2/n) \tag{1}$$

Let $\overline{x}$ denote the observed value of $\overline{X}$.

Case A: Testing H_0: $\mu = \mu_0$ against H_1: $\mu > \mu_0$

In this case an extreme value of $\overline{X}$ will be one greater than μ_0 so that

$$\text{the p-value} = P(\overline{X} \geq \overline{x}) \cong P\left[Z > \frac{\overline{x} - \mu_0}{\text{ESE}(\overline{X})}\right],$$

where $\text{ESE}(\overline{X}) = s/\sqrt{n}$ is the estimated standard error of $\overline{X}$.

Case *B:* Testing H_0: $\mu = \mu_0$ against H_1: $\mu < \mu_0$

In this case

$$\text{the p-value} = P(\overline{X} \le \overline{x}) \cong P\left[Z \le \frac{\overline{x} - \mu_0}{\text{ESE}(\overline{X})}\right]$$

Case C: Testing H_0: $\mu = \mu_0$ against H_1: $\mu \ne \mu_0$.

In this case

(a) if $\overline{x}$ is $> \mu_0$ the p-value $= 2 \times P(\overline{X} \ge \overline{x}) \cong 2 \times P\left[Z \ge \frac{\overline{x} - \mu_0}{\text{ESE}(\overline{X})}\right]$

(b) if $\overline{x}$ is $< \mu_0$ the p-value $= 2 \times P(\overline{X} \le \overline{x}) \cong 2 \times P\left[Z \le \frac{\overline{x} - \mu_0}{\text{ESE}(\overline{X})}\right]$

Example 1

A particular brand of electric light bulb has been designed to have a mean lifetime of 1200 hours. It is suspected that a particular large batch of the bulbs is substandard in the sense that the mean lifetime of the bulbs in the batch is less than 1200 hours. The lifetimes of a random sample of 50 bulbs from the batch had mean 1150 hours and standard deviation 150 hours. Set up appropriate null and alternative hypotheses and determine the approximate p-value of the sample results. State your conclusion about the suspect batch.

Solution

Let μ hours be the mean lifetime of the bulbs in the suspect batch. Since the aim is to determine if the batch is substandard the appropriate test is

$$H_0 : \mu = 1200 \text{ against } H_1 : \mu < 1200 \text{ (substandard)}$$

Assuming that 50 is large enough for the Central Limit Theorem to apply, the sampling distribution of the sample mean is approximately normal with mean μ hours. We shall also assume that the sample size is large enough to use the sample standard deviation as a good approximation to the population standard deviation. Under these assumptions the sampling distribution of the sample mean $\overline{X}$ may be approximated by $N(\mu, 150^2/50) = N(\mu, 450)$.

Since the observed value of $\overline{X}$ is $\overline{x} = 1150$,

$$\text{the p-value} = P(\overline{X} \le 1150 \text{ when } \mu = 1200)$$

$$\cong P\left(Z \le \frac{1150 - 1200}{\sqrt{450}}\right)$$

$$\cong P(Z \le -2.36) \approx 0.009.$$

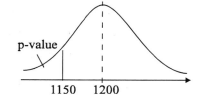

This p-value is small enough to conclude that there is very strong evidence for rejecting H_0 and, therefore, that the batch is substandard.

Example 2

Records of the heights of the policemen in a certain force in 1985 showed that their average height was 185 cm. The question was posed as to whether the average height of policemen in the force in 1995 was different from that in 1985. To answer this question the heights of a random sample of 60 policemen in the force in 1995 were measured in cm. Analysis of these heights gave unbiased estimates of the population mean and variance equal to 182.5 and 22.64, respectively. Carry out an appropriate test to answer the question posed.

Solution

Let μ cm denote the mean height of the policemen in the force in 1995. Appropriate null and alternative hypotheses are :

$$H_0 : \mu = 185 \text{ (no change) against } H_1 : \mu \neq 185 \text{ (change)}$$

Assuming that 60 is large enough for the Central Limit Theorem to apply and for the sample unbiased estimate of the population variance to be reasonably close to the true value, the sampling distribution of the sample mean height $\overline{X}$ of 60 policemen is approximately $N(\mu, 22.64/60)$. Since H_1 is two-sided and the observed value of $\overline{X}$ is $\bar{x} = 182.5$ and is < 185,

$$\text{the p-value} = 2P(\overline{X} \leq 182.5 \text{ when } \mu = 185)$$
$$= 2P\left(Z \leq \frac{182.5 - 185}{\sqrt{22.64/60}} \right)$$
$$\cong 2P(Z \leq -4.07)$$

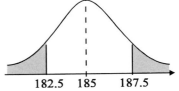

From Table 3 we find that $P(Z \leq -4.07)$ is less than 0.00003, so that the p-value is less than 0.00006, which is extremely small and provides overwhelming evidence against H_0. We can, therefore, very confidently conclude that the mean height in 1995 is less than the mean height in 1985.

Exercise 4.1a

1. A particular type of battery used in calculators is claimed to have a mean operational time of 2000 hours. Tests on a random sample of 200 of these batteries gave a mean operational time of 1997 hours and a standard deviation of 25.5 hours. Test the hypothesis that the claim is correct against the alternative that the mean operational time of such batteries is less than 2000 hours.

2. A fruit wholesaler states that the average weight of the bunches of bananas that he supplies is 800 grams. A retailer weighs a random sample of 80 bunches and calculates the unbiased estimates of the mean and the variance of the weights of such bunches to be

779 grams and 6400 grams^2. Test the hypothesis that the mean weight per bunch is 800 grams against the alternative that it is less than 800 grams.

3. The masses (x grams) of tea in 300 packets were such that $\Sigma x = 39600$ and $\Sigma x^2 = 5231984$. Test the hypothesis that the mean mass per packet of tea is 133 grams against the alternative that it is not.

4. Manufactured nylon cords are claimed to have a mean breaking strength of 18 units. From the breaking strengths of a random sample of 200 such cords the unbiased estimates of the population mean and variance were 17.9 and 2.25, respectively. Test the claim.

5. A medical investigator conducted an experiment to determine whether a new drug would give longer relief from pain than the standard drug currently in use. The two drugs were administered at different times to each of 100 patients. For each patient a record was kept of $w = x - y$, where x hours was the duration of relief from pain with the new drug and y hours was that with the currently used drug. From the 100 values of w obtained it was found that $\Sigma w = 180$ and $\Sigma w^2 = 10324$. Carry out a test and state your conclusion.

6. From a survey of works by a certain author a researcher found that the author averaged 31.5 words per sentence. The researcher suspects that an anonymously written article was actually written by this author. The researcher found that the numbers of words in 80 sentences in the article had a mean of 34 words and a standard deviation of 6.8 words. What conclusion should the researcher draw?

7. The mean mass of sugar in bags of sugar is stated to be 1 kg. The masses (x kg) of sugar found in a random sample of 50 bags of sugar were such that $\Sigma x = 49.5$ and $\Sigma x^2 = 49.04$. Carry out a test to determine if the sample provides enough evidence to conclude that the mean mass of sugar per bag is different from 1 kg.

8. A shopkeeper complained that the average weight of certain packets of biscuits that he buys from a wholesaler is less than the stated weights of 227 grams. The shopkeeper weighed 100 packets and found that their weights had mean 226.8 grams and standard deviation 0.72 grams. Determine whether the shopkeeper is justified in his complaint.

4.1.2 Testing a difference between the means of two distributions

Let X and Y denote two independent normally distributed random variables having means μ_X, μ_Y and standard deviations σ_X, σ_Y, respectively. Consider testing $H_0 : \mu_X - \mu_Y = \delta$ for some specified value of δ. A case of particular interest is that when $\delta = 0$ for testing whether μ_X and μ_Y are equal. Let $\overline{X}$ and $\overline{Y}$, respectively, denote the means of random samples of n_X observations of X and n_Y observations of Y. From

Section 3.2 we know that $\overline{X} - \overline{Y}$ is normally distributed with mean $\mu_X - \mu_Y$ and standard error

$$SE(\overline{X} - \overline{Y}) = \sqrt{\left(\frac{\sigma_X^2}{n_X} + \frac{\sigma_Y^2}{n_Y}\right)} \qquad (1)$$

Denote the observed values of $\overline{X}$ and $\overline{Y}$ by $\overline{x}$ and $\overline{y}$, respectively.

CASE A : $H_0 : \mu_X - \mu_Y = \delta$ against $H_1 : \mu_X - \mu_Y < \delta$.

In this case H_0 should be rejected in favour of H_1 only if $\overline{x} - \overline{y}$ is small compared with δ.

Thus, the p-value $= P(\overline{X} - \overline{Y} \le \overline{x} - \overline{y}$ when H_0 is true)

$$= P\left(Z \le \frac{\overline{x} - \overline{y} - \delta}{SE(\overline{X} - \overline{Y})}\right) \qquad (2)$$

CASE B : $H_0 : \mu_X - \mu_Y = \delta$ against $H_1 : \mu_X - \mu_Y > \delta$.

In this case

the p-value $= P(\overline{X} - \overline{Y} \ge \overline{x} - \overline{y}$ when H_0 is true)

$$= P\left(Z \ge \frac{\overline{x} - \overline{y} - \delta}{SE(\overline{X} - \overline{Y})}\right) \qquad (3)$$

CASE C : $H_0 : \mu_X - \mu_Y = \delta$ against $H_1 : \mu_X - \mu_Y \ne \delta$.

In this case H_0 should be rejected if $\overline{x} - \overline{y}$ is large or small compared with δ.

(a) If $\overline{x} - \overline{y}$ is $< \delta$,

$$\text{the p-value} = 2P\left(\overline{X} - \overline{Y} \le \frac{\overline{x} - \overline{y} - \delta}{SE(\overline{X} - \overline{Y})}\right) \qquad (4a)$$

(b) If $\overline{x} - \overline{y}$ is $> \delta$,

$$\text{the p-value} = 2P\left(\overline{X} - \overline{Y} \ge \frac{\overline{x} - \overline{y} - \delta}{SE(\overline{X} - \overline{Y})}\right) \qquad (4b)$$

Example 1

A firm has two precision grinding machines, A and B, which produce cylindrical rods of mean diameter 2.500 cm. The diameters of the rods produced on machine A are normally distributed with standard deviation 0.01 cm and the rods produced on machine B are normally distributed with standard deviation 0.015 cm. The composition of steel the firm receives from its supplier is changed slightly. Random samples of 10 rods from the outputs of machines A and B had mean diameters of 2.535 cm and 2.552 cm, respectively. Assuming that the standard deviations of the diameters of the rods are unchanged, test the hypothesis that the mean diameters produced by the two machines will still be equal.

Solution

Let X and Y, respectively, denote the diameters of randomly selected rods from machines A and B, and let μ_X and μ_Y denote the means of X and Y. We need to test

$$H_0 : \mu_X = \mu_Y \text{ against } H_1 : \mu_X \neq \mu_Y.$$

Let $\overline{X}$ and $\overline{Y}$ denote the sample means. Since $X \sim N(\mu_X, 0.01^2)$, and $Y \sim N(\mu_Y, 0.015^2)$, it follows that $\overline{X} \sim N(\mu_X, 0.01^2/10)$, and $\overline{Y} \sim N(\mu_Y, 0.015^2/10)$, and since these are independent, it follows from (1) above that $\overline{X} - \overline{Y}$ is normally distributed with mean $\mu_X - \mu_Y$ and standard error

$$SE(\overline{X} - \overline{Y}) = \sqrt{\left(\frac{0.01^2}{10} + \frac{0.015^2}{10}\right)} \cong 0.0057.$$

The observed value of $\overline{X} - \overline{Y} = 2.535 - 2.552 = -0.017$. Since this is less than zero and H_1 is two-sided, from (4a) above with $\delta = 0$, we have

$$\text{the p-value} = 2P\left(Z \leq -\frac{0.017}{0.0057}\right) \cong 2P(Z \leq -2.98)$$

$$\cong 2 \times 0.00144 \approx 0.0029.$$

Hence, there is very strong evidence for rejecting H_0, and we can conclude that $\mu_Y > \mu_X$. That is, with the new composition of the steel, the mean diameter of rods produced on machine B is greater than that produced on machine A.

The general results given previously can also be used to find approximate p-values when the distributions are not known to be normal provided the sample sizes are large. Furthermore, again provided that the sample sizes are large, we can also approximate $SE(\overline{X} - \overline{Y})$ by

$$ESE(\overline{X} - \overline{Y}) = \sqrt{\left(\frac{s_X^2}{n_X} + \frac{s_Y^2}{n_Y}\right)} \qquad (5)$$

where s_X^2 and s_Y^2 are the samples unbiased estimates of σ_X^2 and σ_Y^2, respectively. These approximations are used in the following example.

Example 2

A manufacturer of electrical equipment purchases components in bulk. There are two possible suppliers, A and B, of a particular type of component required by the manufacturer. Since components from A are the more expensive to purchase, the manufacturer calculated that he would purchase from A only if the average lifetime of A's components exceeds that of B's by more than 200 hours. The lifetimes, in hours, of a random sample of 80 components produced by A gave unbiased estimates of the mean and variance of the lifetimes equal to 1258 and 8836, respectively. The lifetimes, in hours, of a random sample of 60 components produced by B gave unbiased estimates of the mean and variance of the lifetimes equal to 1029 and 4624, respectively. Carry out a test to advise the manufacturer which supplier he should use.

Solution

Let μ_A and μ_B denote the mean lifetimes, in hours, of components produced by A and B, respectively. Since the manufacturer is interested in determining whether $\mu_A - \mu_B$ exceeds 200, the appropriate null and alternative hypotheses are

$$H_0 : \mu_A - \mu_B = 200 \quad \text{and} \quad H_1 : \mu_A - \mu_B > 200.$$

Since $n_A = 80$, $\overline{x}_A = 1258$, $s_A{}^2 = 8836$ and $n_B = 60$, $\overline{x}_B = 1029$, $s_B{}^2 = 4624$ it follows from (5) above that the estimated standard error of $\overline{X}_A - \overline{X}_B$ is

$$\text{ESE}(\overline{X}_A - \overline{X}_B) = \left(\frac{8836}{80} + \frac{4624}{60} \right)^{\frac{1}{2}} \cong 13.6937.$$

Thus, using (3) above we have

$$\text{the p-value} \cong P(\overline{X}_A - \overline{X}_B \geq \overline{x}_A - \overline{x}_B \text{ when } H_0 \text{ is true})$$
$$\cong P\left(Z \geq \frac{1258 - 1029 - 200}{13.6937} \right) \cong P(Z \geq 2.12) \cong 0.017$$

Thus, the samples provide strong evidence against H_0 so that the recommendation to the manufacturer is to purchase the components from supplier A.

Exercise 4.1b

1. A test is required of $H_0 : \mu_1 = \mu_2$ against $H_1 : \mu_1 \neq \mu_2$, where μ_1 and μ_2 are the means of independent normal distributions whose variances are 24.86 and 12.42, respectively. A random sample of 25 observations from the first distribution had mean $\overline{x}_1 = 80.9$, while a random sample of 36 observations from the second distribution had mean $\overline{x}_2 = 78.4$. Perform the test and state your conclusion.

2. The mean of a random sample of 12 observations from $N(\mu_X, 16)$ was 45.82, and that of a random sample of 20 observations from $N(\mu_Y, 24)$ was 42.75. Test $H_0 : \mu_X = \mu_Y$ against $H_1 : \mu_X > \mu_Y$.

3. Jim and John are keen members of the Aberponty Onion Growing Society, and each claims to grow the larger onions. To test their claims, the secretary of the Society gives each of them 12 onion sets at the beginning of the growing season and they plant these in their gardens. At the end of the season, Jim has 12 onions whose total weight is 13.25 kg, while John was unlucky with one onion and ends up with 11 onions whose total weight is

12.69 kg. The secretary knows from experience that, independent of the mean weight, the weights of onions are normally distributed with standard deviation 0.05 kg. Use the data to determine which of the two grows the larger onions on average.

4.   It has been claimed that girls do better, on average, than boys in a Statistics examination.   From random samples of 60 girls and 80 boys who sat a Statistics examination, the girls' marks (x) and the boys' marks (y) were such that

$$\Sigma x = 3054,\ \Sigma x^2 = 157572\ ;\ \Sigma y = 3844,\ \Sigma y^2 = 189760.$$

Test whether the claim is justified on the basis of these results.

5.   To compare the speeds of two different methods, A and B, of performing a specific task, the task was performed using method A by 120 men and using method B by 146 men.   The times (x minutes) taken by the men using method A and the times (y minutes) taken by the men using method B were such that

$$\bar{x} = 17.1,\ \Sigma(x - \bar{x})^2 = 320\ ;\ \bar{y} = 17.4,\ \Sigma(y - \bar{y})^2 = 178.$$

Calculate the estimated standard error of the difference between the two sample means. Determine whether either method may be claimed to be the quicker, on average.

6.   A union spokesman complained to company A that labourers employed there were paid lower wages on average than those employed by company B.   In a randomly chosen sample of 50 labourers employed by A their weekly wages had a mean of £112.20 and a standard deviation of £8.80, while in a random sample of 50 labourers employed by B the mean and the standard deviation of their wages were £114.70 and £5.20, respectively. Test whether the claim made by the union spokesman is justified.

7.   A claim was made that the average salary paid to teachers in independent schools exceeded that paid to teachers in state schools by more than £2400 per year.   The salaries (in thousands of pounds) of a random sample of 50 teachers in independent schools gave unbiased estimates of the population mean and variance equal to 25.4 and 3.58, respectively.   Test the hypothesis that the mean salary paid to teachers in independent schools is £2400 more than that paid to teachers in state schools against the alternative that the difference is greater than £2400.

8.   It is required to test if the mean height of men living in a certain county is 15 cm more than the mean height of women living in the county, against the alternative that the difference is greater than 15 cm.   From the heights of a random sample of 100 men it was found that the unbiased estimates of the population mean and variance were 178.1 cm and 25.12 cm^2.   From the heights of a random sample of 100 women it was found that the unbiased estimates of the population mean and variance were 164.2 cm and 15.91 cm^2. Carry out the test and state your conclusion.

9. In an investigation into the effectiveness of a particular course in speed reading, a group of 500 students was split at random into two equal groups, A and B. The students in group A were given the course, while those in group B were not. At the end of the course each student was asked to read the same passage and the time taken was measured. The mean and variance of the times taken (in seconds) by each group were as follows :

Group A : mean 139.2 , variance 10

Group B : mean 144.7 , variance 20

Test whether the course is effective in reducing the mean reading time by more than 5 seconds.

10. Two types of battery were compared for the length of time that they lasted. The results of tests carried out on samples of the two types of battery are given in the following table.

Battery Type	Number tested	Sample mean	Sample standard deviation
A	200	1995	25.5
B	150	2005	32.8

Stating clearly any assumptions you make, test whether the mean lengths of times are equal for the two types of battery.

4.2 Significance testing

Introduction

Now consider the significance testing approach to the situations considered in Section 4.1. The approach will be an adaptation of that given in Section 3.3 of the S2 book. In particular, recall the definition of a significance level as being the probability that the null hypothesis will be rejected when it is true. As in Section 3.3 of the S2 book there are two problems to consider, namely:

(a) determining the significance level of a given decision rule,

(b) determining a decision rule having a specified significance level.

Recall that one method for dealing with (b) is to calculate the sample p-value and to reject the null hypothesis only if it is less than the specified significance level. An alternative method is to calculate the z-value [an observation from N (0,1)] and to reject the null hypothesis only if it is in the critical region for the specified significance level. This latter method will be used in the examples of the following subsections, but the former method is equally good; calculating a sample p-value has been covered in Section 4.1.

4.2.1 Significance testing a distribution mean

Let X denote a random variable whose distribution is unknown. A large sample of n observations of X is to be used to test the null hypothesis H_0: $\mu = \mu_0$, where $\mu = E(X)$. By the Central Limit Theorem the sampling distribution of the sample mean $\overline{X}$ may be approximated by a normal distribution having mean μ and approximate variance s^2/n, where s^2 is the sample unbiased estimate of Var(X). Thus, assuming that H_0 is true

$$\overline{X} \approx N(\mu_0, s^2/n)$$

or, equivalently, $\quad Z \equiv \dfrac{\overline{X} - \mu_0}{s/\sqrt{n}} \approx N(0,1)$.

We can then base our decision on the observed value

$$z = \frac{\overline{x} - \mu_0}{s/\sqrt{n}} \tag{1}$$

where $\overline{x}$ is the observed sample mean.

Case A: Testing H_0: $\mu = \mu_0$ against H_1: $\mu > \mu_0$ with significance level α.

In this case, if H_1 is true, we would expect z given by (1) to be large and positive so the decision is to reject H_0 if the observed z is $\geq z_\alpha$, where z_α is such that $P(Z \geq z_\alpha) = \alpha$, whose value can be read from Table 4.

Case B: Testing H_0: $\mu = \mu_0$ against H_1: $\mu < \mu_0$ with significance level α

Modifying the above in an obvious manner the decision in this case is to reject H_0 if the observed z given by (1) is $\leq -z_\alpha$.

Case C: Testing H_0: $\mu = \mu_0$ against H_1: $\mu \neq \mu_0$ with significance level α.

As previously with a two-sided alternative hypothesis we have to allow for the possibilities that, when H_1 is true, the observed value of z may be large and positive or large and negative. Modifying what we did in Section 3.3.1 of the S2 book, the decision is to reject H_0 if the **numerical** value of z is $\geq z_{\frac{1}{2}\alpha}$.

Recall from Section 3.3.1 that the approximate $100(1 - \alpha)$% confidence limits for μ are

$$\overline{x} \pm z_{\frac{1}{2}\alpha} \times s/\sqrt{n}$$

It is readily verified that any μ_0 outside the interval having these limits will be rejected when the significance level is α. Note well that this is always true when testing a null hypothesis against a two-sided alternative.

Example 1

A researcher for a manufacturer of string has claimed that a particular type of coating applied to the string would increase its mean breaking strength from its present value of 7.2 kg. The coating was applied to a random sample of 60 pieces of string and their breaking strengths (x kg) were such that

$$\sum x = 456 \quad \text{and} \quad \sum x^2 = 3540.$$

Use a significance level of 5% to determine whether or not the researcher's claim is correct.

Solution

Let μ kg denote the mean breaking strength of coated pieces of string. We need to test

$\qquad$ H_0: $\mu = 7.2$ against H_1: $\mu > 7.2$ with significance level 0.05.

Let $\overline{X}$ kg denote the mean breaking strength of a random sample of 60 pieces of the string. From the given sample results

$$\overline{x} = \frac{656}{60} = 7.4$$

and the unbiased estimate of the variance of the breaking strengths is

$$s^2 = \frac{1}{59}\left(3540 - \frac{456^2}{60}\right) = 1.2610$$

Assuming that n = 60 is large enough to justify (i) the use of the Central Limit Theorem and (ii) taking s^2 as being close to the population variance, we have

$$\overline{X} \approx N(7.2, \frac{1 \cdot 2610}{60} = 0.0210) \quad \text{when } H_0 \text{ is true.}$$

$$\Rightarrow \quad Z \equiv (\overline{X} - 7.2)/\sqrt{0 \cdot 0210} \approx N(0,1)$$

The observed value of Z is

$$z = \frac{7 \cdot 4 - 7 \cdot 2}{\sqrt{0 \cdot 0210}} = 1.30$$

As the significance level is 0·05 the critical value of z is $z_{0 \cdot 05} = 1.645$ (from Table 4). Since the observed z is less than the critical z we cannot reject H_0 and our conclusion is that there is insufficient evidence to endorse the researcher's claim.

[It is left as an exercise to show that the sample p-value is approximately 0.0968 which is greater than 0.05 and leads to the same conclusion as given above.]

Example 2 (Example 1 of Section 4.1.1)

A particular brand of electric light bulb has been designed to have a mean lifetime of 1200 hours. It is suspected that a particular large batch of the bulbs is substandard in the sense that the mean lifetime of the bulbs in the batch is less than 1200 hours. The lifetimes of a random sample 50 bulbs from the suspect batch had mean 1150 hours and standard deviation 150 hours. Use a 1% significance level to carry out the appropriate test.

Solution

Let X hours denote the lifetime of a randomly chosen bulb from the suspect batch and let μ hours denote the mean lifetime of the bulbs in the batch. Since it is suspected that μ < 1200 we need to test

H_0: μ = 1200 against H_1: μ < 1200 with significance level 0.01

Here, n = 50, $\overline{x}$ = 1150 and s = 150 (on assuming that this is the square root of the unbiased estimate of the population variance). Thus, when H_0 is true

$$\overline{X} \approx N(1200, 150^2/50 = 450)$$

$$\Rightarrow \quad Z \equiv (\overline{X} - 1200)/\sqrt{450} \approx N(0,1).$$

The observed value is z = $(1150 - 1200)/\sqrt{450} = -2.36$.

The critical region in this case is z < - $z_{0 \cdot 01}$ = –2.326. Since the observed z is less than this critical value we can reject H_0 at the 1% significance level and conclude that the batch is substandard. [In Example 1 of Section 4.1.1 we showed that the sample p-value was 0.009 which is less than the significance level and leads to the same conclusion]

Example 3 (Example 2 of Section 4.1.1)

Records of the heights of the policemen in a certain force in 1985 showed that their mean height was 185 cm. The question was posed as to whether the mean height of the policemen in the force in 1995 was different from that in 1985. To answer this question the heights of a random sample of 60 policemen in the force in 1995 were measured in cm. Analysis of the results gave unbiased estimates of the population mean and variance equal to 182.5 and 22.64, respectively. Carry out the appropriate test assuming a significance level of approximately 0.02.

Solution

Let μ cm denote the mean height of the policemen in 1995. We need to test $H_0: \mu = 185$ against $H_1: \mu \neq 185$ with a significance level of approximately 0·02. From the given sample results

$$n = 60, \ \overline{x} = 182·5, \ s^2 = 22·64.$$

Let $\overline{X}$ cm denote the mean height of a random sample of 60 policemen in 1995. Then assuming that H_0 is true

$$\overline{X} \approx N\left(185, \ \frac{22·64}{60} = 0·3773 \right)$$

$$\Rightarrow \quad Z \equiv (\overline{X} - 185)/\sqrt{0·3773} \ \approx N(0,1)$$

Since H_1 is two-sided the appropriate observed value of Z is

$$z = \left| 182·5 - 185 \right| / \sqrt{0·3773} = 4·07 .$$

The critical region in this case is $z \geq z_{0·01} = 2.326$ (from Table 4). Since the observed z is in this critical region we reject H_0, and since $\overline{x}$ is < 185 we can conclude that the mean height of policemen in 1995 is less than that in 1985.

[In Example 2 of Section 4.1.1 we showed that the sample p-value was 0.009 which is less than the significance level of 0.02 so that the conclusion is the same. It is left as an exercise to show that the approximate 98% confidence interval for μ is (181.07,183.93). Since 185 is outside this interval we reject H_0 at the 2% significance level and the conclusion is as above. In fact, this confidence interval shows that any specified $\mu_0 < 181.07$ or > 183.93 would be rejected at the 2% significance level]

Exercise 4.2a

1. A random sample of 100 fibres taken from a large bundle had breaking strengths whose mean was 15.28 and whose standard deviation was 0.35. Determine whether this sample provides sufficient evidence to justify concluding that the mean strength of such fibres is greater than 15.2. Use a significance level of 5%.

2. A random variable X has unknown mean μ and unknown standard deviation σ. A random sample of 50 observations of X had sum 2625 and sum of squares 137950. Test the hypothesis $\mu = 52$ against the alternative hypothesis that $\mu \neq 52$ using a significance level of (a) 5%, (b) 2%.

3. The sum of the lengths (in cm) of 100 manufactured articles was found to be 305 and the sum of the squares of the lengths was 1225. Test, using a 5% significance level, the hypothesis that the mean length of the articles is 3 cm.

4. A shopkeeper complained that the average weight of chocolate bars of a certain brand bought from a wholesaler is less than the stated value of 8.5 grams. The shopkeeper weighed 100 bars and found that their weights had mean 8.36 grams and standard deviation 0.72 grams. Using a 5% significance level, determine whether or not the shopkeeper is justified in his complaint.

5. The marks (x) obtained by a random sample of 250 candidates in a large entry examination were such that $\Sigma x = 11872$ and $\Sigma x^2 = 646193$. Let μ denote the mean mark for all the candidates in the examination. Suppose that the hypothesis $\mu = 49.5$ is to be tested against the alternative that $\mu < 49.5$ using a significance level of α. Determine the set of values of α for which the hypothesis $\mu = 49.5$ should be rejected.

6. It is claimed that the average mileage traveled per year by midwives in carrying out their duties was 12000. However, it was counter-claimed that the average was less than 12000. For a random sample of 100 midwives it was found that the distances they had traveled on duty during the preceding year had mean 11500 miles and standard deviation 2400 miles. Using a significance level of 1% test the claim made against the counter-claim.

7. An ice-cream producer claims that the fat content of his ice-cream is 10%. An analysis of 50 cartons of the ice-cream gave a mean fat content of 10.3% and a standard deviation of 1.4%. Use a 5% significance level to test the producer's claim.

4.2.2 Significance testing a difference between the means of two distributions

Let $\overline{X}$ denote the mean of a random sample of n_X observations from $N(\mu_X, \sigma_X^2)$ and let $\overline{Y}$ denote a random sample of n_Y observations from $N(\mu_Y, \sigma_Y^2)$ and suppose it is required to test the null hypothesis $H_0 : \mu_X - \mu_Y = \delta$ for some specified value for δ.

The theoretical results are readily deduced from those in Section 4.2.1. on replacing $\overline{X}$ by

$$\overline{X} - \overline{Y}, \mu_0 \text{ by } \delta \text{ and } SE(\overline{X}) \text{ by } SE(\overline{X} - \overline{Y}) = \sqrt{\left(\frac{\sigma_X^2}{n_X} + \frac{\sigma_Y^2}{n_Y}\right)}; \text{ see also Section 4.1.2.}$$

The procedures for significance testing are demonstrated in the following examples.

Example 1

X and Y are two independent normally distributed random variables each having standard deviation 5. The means μ_X and μ_Y, respectively, of the distributions are unknown. It is required to test $H_0 : \mu_X - \mu_Y = 2$ against $H_1 : \mu_X - \mu_Y > 2$ using the values obtained in random samples of 50 observations of each of X and Y.

(a) Find the significance level of the decision rule which will reject H_0 if $\overline{X} - \overline{Y} \geq 4$, where $\overline{X}$ and $\overline{Y}$ are the sample means.

(b) Find the decision rule if the significance level is to be 0.01.

(c) Given that the observed sample means were $\overline{x} = 9.5$ and $\overline{y} = 5.8$ find the smallest significance level for H_0 to be rejected.

Solution

Given that X and Y are independent with $X \sim N(\mu_X, 25)$ and $Y \sim N(\mu_Y, 25)$ and that $\overline{X}$ and $\overline{Y}$ are the means of random samples of size 50 each it follows that the sampling distribution of $\overline{X} - \overline{Y}$ is normal with mean $\mu - \lambda$ and standard error

$$SE(\overline{X} - \overline{Y}) = \sqrt{\left(\frac{25}{50} + \frac{25}{50}\right)} = 1.$$

(a) The significance level of the given decision rule is

$$P(\overline{X} - \overline{Y} \geq 4 \text{ when } H_0 \text{ is true}) = P\left(Z \geq \frac{4-2}{1}\right) = P(Z \geq 2) = 0.02275.$$

(b) Consider the decision rule

$$\text{Reject } H_0 \text{ if } \overline{X} - \overline{Y} \geq c.$$

The significance level of this rule is

$$P(\overline{X} - \overline{Y} \geq c \text{ when } H_0 \text{ is true}) = P\left(Z \geq \frac{c-2}{1}\right) = P(Z \geq c - 2).$$

For a significance level of 0.01, c must be such that $P(Z \geq c - 2) = 0.01$.

Referring to Table 4 we find $c - 2 = 2.576$, so that $c = 4.576$.

Thus, the decision rule having a 1% significance level is :

$$\text{Reject } H_0 \text{ if } \overline{X} - \overline{Y} \geq 4.576.$$

(c) The smallest significance level for H_0 to be rejected is the p-value. Since

$$\overline{x} - \overline{y} = 9.5 - 5.8 = 3.7 \text{ is} > 2,$$

$$\text{the p-value} = P(\overline{X} - \overline{Y} \geq 3.7 \text{ when } \mu - \lambda = 2)$$

$$= P\left(Z \geq \frac{3.7 - 2}{1}\right) = P(Z \geq 1.7) \cong 0.0446.$$

So, for the observed sample means, H_0 should be rejected only if the chosen significance level is ≥ 0.045 (4.5%).

Example 2 (compare Example 1 of Section 4.1.2)

A firm has two precision grinding machines, A and B, each of which produces cylindrical rods of mean diameter 2.500 cm. The diameters of the rods produced on machine A are normally distributed with standard deviation 0.01 cm and the rods produced on machine B are normally distributed with standard deviation 0.015 cm. The composition of the steel the firm receives from its supplier is changed slightly. Random samples of 10 rods from the outputs of machines A and B had mean diameters of 2.535 cm and 2.552 cm, respectively. Assuming that the standard deviations of the diameters of the rods are unchanged, test the hypothesis that the mean diameters produced by the two machines are still equal using a 1% significance level.

Solution

Let X and Y denote the diameters (in cm) of randomly selected rods from machines A and B, respectively, and let μ_X and μ_Y denote the mean diameters. We need to test

$$H_0: \mu_X = \mu_Y \text{ against } H_1: \mu_X \neq \mu_Y \text{ with significance level } 0.01$$

Denoting the sample means (each of size 10) by $\overline{X}$ and $\overline{Y}$ it follows from the result given in Section 4.1.2 that, when H_0 is true

$$\overline{X} - \overline{Y} \sim N\left(0, \frac{0\cdot01^2}{10} + \frac{0\cdot015^2}{10} = 0\cdot0000325\right)$$

$$\Rightarrow \quad Z \equiv (\overline{X} - \overline{Y})/\sqrt{0\cdot0000325} \sim N(0,1).$$

Since H_1 is two-sided we calculate

$$z = \left|2\cdot535 - 2\cdot552\right|/\sqrt{0\cdot0000325} = 2.98.$$

Since H_1 is two-sided and the significance level is 0.01 the critical value of z is $z_{0.05} = 2.326$. The observed z (2.98) is in the critical region so we reject H_0 and conclude that $\mu_Y > \mu_X$ (since $\overline{y} > \overline{x}$).

Alternatively, we showed in Example 1 of Section 4.1.2 that the samples p-value was approximately 0.0029, which is less than the significance level (0.01), so that the conclusion is as given above. Since H_1 is two-sided, a third method for answering this question is to calculate the 99% confidence limits for $\mu_X - \mu_Y$ and to reject H_0 if the two limits are of same sign. Here, the 99% confidence limits are -0.0023 and -0.0017.

If nothing is known about the distributions of X and Y then provided we have large samples we can use the Central Limit Theorem and the sample unbiased estimates of the population variances to carry out an approximate test. This is illustrated in the following example.

Example 3

A new fertiliser for tomato plants is claimed to result in higher yields. The new fertiliser was applied to 100 plants and the standard fertiliser was applied to another 100 plants. The yields (x) of tomatoes from plants given the new fertiliser were such that
$$\sum x = 1030.0 \text{ and } \sum x^2 = 11045.59,$$
while the yields (y) from the plants given the standard fertiliser were such that
$$\sum y = 990.0 \text{ and } \sum y^2 = 10079.19 \,.$$
Use a 5% significance level to test whether the results justify the claim made for the new fertiliser.

Solution

Let X denote the yield from a plant given the new fertiliser and let Y denote the yield from a plant given the standard fertiliser. Denoting the mean yields by μ_X and μ_Y, respectively, we need to test
$$H_0: \mu_X = \mu_Y \text{ against } H_1: \mu_X > \mu_Y \text{ with significance level } 0.05$$
The sample sizes are large enough to use the Central Limit Theorem and to replace the variances of the distributions by their sample unbiased estimates. Assuming that H_0 is true the sampling distribution of $\overline{X} - \overline{Y}$ is approximately normal with mean 0 and estimated variance $\dfrac{s_X^2}{100} + \dfrac{s_Y^2}{100}$, where

$$s_X^2 = \frac{1}{99}\left\{\sum x^2 - \left(\sum x\right)^2 / 100\right\} = \frac{1}{99}\{11045.59 - 1030^2/100\} = 4.41$$

$$s_Y^2 = \frac{1}{99}\left\{\sum y^2 - \left(\sum y\right)^2 / 100\right\} = \frac{1}{99}\{10079.19 - 990^2/100\} = 2.81$$

Assuming that H_0 is true
$$\overline{X} - \overline{Y} \approx N\left(0, \frac{4\cdot41}{100} + \frac{2\cdot81}{100} = 0\cdot0722\right)$$
$$\Rightarrow \quad Z \equiv (\overline{X} - \overline{Y})/\sqrt{0\cdot0722} \approx N(0,1)$$
The observed value of Z is
$$z = (\overline{x} - \overline{y})/\sqrt{0\cdot0722} = (10.3 - 9.9)/\sqrt{0\cdot0722} = 1.49$$

Since H_1 is one-sided and the significance level is 0.05 the critical value of z is $z_{0.05} = 1.645$ (from Table 4). The observed z is not in the critical region and, consequently, there is insufficient evidence to conclude that the new fertiliser will give a higher mean yield than the standard fertiliser.

[Alternatively, the p-value may be shown to be $P(Z > 1.49) = 0.0681$ (from Table 3) which is greater than the significance level so that the conclusion is that given above.]

Exercise 4.2b

1. The random variables X and Y are independent with $X \sim N(\mu, 25)$ and $Y \sim N(\lambda, 16)$. It is required to test $H_0 : \mu - \lambda = 10$ against $H_1 : \mu - \lambda < 10$ based on the values obtained in a random sample of 10 observations of X and 12 observations of Y.
(a) Find the significance level of the test that will reject H_0 only if $\overline{X} - \overline{Y} \leq 7.5$, where $\overline{X}$ and $\overline{Y}$ are the sample means.
(b) Given that the observed values of the sample means were $\overline{x} = 35.96$ and $\overline{y} = 29.21$ what conclusion should be drawn if the significance level is 5%?

2. The random variables X and Y are normally distributed each having standard deviation 43. A random sample of 20 observations of X had mean 2186, while a random sample of 20 observations of Y had mean 2162. Use a 5% significance level to test whether the means of the two distributions are equal.

3. Suppose that the lifetimes of car tyres are normally distributed with standard deviation 3000 miles. A random sample of 9 tyres of brand A had a mean lifetime of 26000 miles, while a random sample of 9 tyres of brand B had a mean lifetime of 23400 miles. Brand A tyres are more expensive than brand B tyres. Using a 5% significance level, test whether one is justified in concluding that the more expensive tyres have the longer mean lifetime.

4. Measurements of the refractive index of glass made by a certain refractometer are known to be subject to errors which are normally distributed with zero mean and standard deviation 0.004. Two samples of glass fragments were examined to see if they could have come from the same source. The first sample consisted of 6 fragments and their mean refractive index was found to be 1.525. The second sample consisted of 5 fragments and their mean refractive index was found to be 1.528. The fragments in the first sample came from a broken window at the scene of a burglary, while those in the second sample were found on a suspect's clothing. Use a 10% significance level to test the hypothesis that the samples are of the same glass.

5. The random variables X and Y are known to be independent and normally distributed with means μ and λ, and standard deviations 2 and 4, respectively. A test is required of

the hypothesis that $\mu = \lambda$ against the alternative that $\mu \neq \lambda$. The test is to be based on the means of random samples of 16 observations of X and 25 observations of Y.

(a) One possible test is to reject $\mu = \lambda$ only if the numerical difference between the two sample means exceeds a certain value c. Obtain the value of c for this test to have a significance level of 0.05.

(b) Another possible test is to reject $\mu = \lambda$ only if the 95% confidence intervals for μ and for λ do not overlap. Show that the significance level of this test is approximately 0.007.

6. The lengths (in cm) of 100 articles manufactured in one section of a factory summed to 305 and the sum of the squares of the lengths was 1225. The lengths (in cm) of 50 such articles manufactured in a different section summed to 180 and the sum of the squares of their lengths was 746. Test, at the 5% significance level, the hypothesis that the mean lengths of articles manufactured in the two sections are equal.

7. In a study to assess the effect of fluoride in toothpaste, 100 children used a toothpaste containing fluoride and 100 children used one not containing fluoride. Over the period of the study the group using fluoride toothpaste averaged 6.7 new cavities per child, while the other group averaged 7.5 new cavities per child. The sample standard deviations for the groups were 2.8 and 2.3, respectively. Using a significance level of approximately 5% test the hypothesis that the use of fluoride in toothpaste has no beneficial effect against the alternative that it reduces the number of cavities.

8. An oil company has produced an additive for petrol which is claimed will reduce fuel consumption. To test the claim 100 cars were driven with and 120 cars were driven without the additive. The numbers of miles per gallon (x) traveled by the 100 cars and the number of miles per gallon (y) traveled by the 120 cars were such that

$$\Sigma x = 4230, \ \Sigma x^2 = 179820 \ ; \ \Sigma y = 5016, \ \Sigma y^2 = 212048$$

Using a 5% significance level, test the oil company's claim and state your conclusion.

9. In order to test which of two methods, A and B, is the quicker in completing a particular task, two groups of workers were chosen at random. One group consisted of 78 workers who used method A, while the other group consisted of 92 workers who used method B. The times (x minutes) taken by the first group were such that $\Sigma x = 998.4$ and $\Sigma x^2 = 12890.40$, while the times (y minutes) by the second group were such that $\Sigma y = 1122.4$ and $\Sigma y^2 = 14308.44$.

(a) Test, using a significance level of approximately 10%, the hypothesis that the mean times are equal for both methods.

(b) Calculate the least significance level for which the hypothesis in (a) would be rejected.

10. The heights (x metres) of a random sample of 120 male students and the heights (y metres) of a random sample of 160 female students were such that :

$$\Sigma x = 198, \ \Sigma x^2 = 327 \ ; \ \Sigma y = 248, \ \Sigma y^2 = 385.$$

Test using a significance level of approximately 1%, the hypothesis that the mean height of male students exceeds the mean height of female students by more than 0.08 metres.

Miscellaneous Questions on Chapter 4

1. The number of long-distance telephone calls made by staff at the university averaged 3.75 per day. The head of the Mathematics department wondered if the average number of long-distance calls made per day by his staff was different from 3.75. The head decided to keep a record over 40 days of the number of long-distance calls made by his staff. He found that the numbers of long-distance calls made per day had mean 4.175 and standard deviation 2.42. What should the head conclude if the significance level is 0.05?

2. The stock manager of a mail order firm frequently buys a bulk supply of manila envelopes from supplier A. Another supplier B is now being considered. The stock manager will switch to B only if its envelopes have a greater mean tearing weight than that by supplier A. Random samples of envelopes from each supplier are obtained and the tearing weights (kg) of the sampled envelopes gave the following results.

Supplier	Sample size	Sum of tearing weights	Sum of squares of tearing weights
A	120	3540	104610
B	100	2992	89700

Set up appropriate null and alternative hypotheses. Use the results of the samples to determine the p-value. State which supplier the stock manager should use if he is prepared to risk a probability of 0.01 of switching to B when in fact the mean tearing weight of envelopes A and B are equal.

3. It is required to test $H_0 : \mu_1 = \mu_2$ against $H_1 : \mu_1 \neq \mu_2$, where μ_1 and μ_2 are the means of independent normal distributions having standard deviations 5 and 4, respectively. A random sample of 20 observations from the first distribution had mean $\bar{x}_1 = 79.5$, and a random sample of 16 observations from the second distribution had mean $\bar{x}_2 = 76.4$. Perform the test, using a 5% significance level, (a) by first finding an appropriate confidence interval for $\mu_1 - \mu_2$, (b) by calculating the p-value. The conclusion you draw from the test should be clearly stated.

4. A large company A proposes a takeover of a smaller company B. Company B claims that its shareholders' opinions are equally divided for and against the takeover on the basis of the terms offered, whereas company A claims that more than half of B's shareholders are in favour of accepting the offer. To test the two claims the opinions of a random sample of 20 of B's shareholders will be sought. Set up suitable null and alternative hypotheses for a significance test. Let X denote the number of the sampled shareholders who favour the takeover. If A's claim is to be accepted if $X \geq 13$ find the significance level of the test.

5. Two types, A and B, of packaging for a new product are being considered. To determine which to use it is decided to canvass the opinions of 100 potential customers. Each customer is to be asked to award a score, from 1 to 10, for each type of packaging. Let the random variables X_A and X_B denote a customer's scores for type A and type B, respectively, and let $Y = X_A - X_B$. It was found that the observed values (y) of Y for the sampled 100 customers where such that $\Sigma y = 104$ and $\Sigma y^2 = 1559$. Set up appropriate null and alternative hypotheses for testing which type (if any) of packaging has the higher rating on average. Assuming a significance level of 0.01 what conclusion can be drawn?

6. (1996, S2) When a scientist uses an instrument to measure the concentration of a solution, the measurement obtained can be assumed to be normally distributed with mean equal to the actual concentration and standard deviation 2.5 (in appropriate units). The scientist makes 6 independent measurements on each of two solutions, *A* and *B*, and obtains the following results.

> Solution *A*   41.2, 44.6, 43.0, 46.1, 45.8, 39.7
> Solution *B*   45.1, 47.9, 48.4, 42.6, 47.7, 48.8

(a) Calculate the means of the two sets of measurements and verify that the difference, d, between the two means is 3.35. (1)

(b) The scientist believes that the concentrations of solutions A and B are equal.

(i) Calculate, correct to two decimal places, the p-value of the above value of d, assuming a two-sided alternative hypothesis. (4)

(ii) State your conclusion regarding the scientist's belief. (1)

7. (1996, A3) The manager of a large hotel has to decide which of two brands of light bulbs, brand A or brand B, he should use in the hotel. The prices of the two brands are the same and he therefore decides to compare their lifetimes by monitoring samples of the two brands.

(a) For each light bulb in a random sample of 100 brand A bulbs, the manager measured the lifetime, x thousand hours, and found that $\Sigma x = 231.6$; $\Sigma x^2 = 566.38$.

Calculate unbiased estimates for (i) the mean μ_A, (ii) the variance of the lifetemes of brand A bulbs. (3)

(b) Unbiased estimates of 2.408 and 0.3212 for the mean μ_B and the variance, respectively, of the lifetimes (in thousand hours) of brand B were calculated from the random sample of 150 such bulbs. Stating suitable null and alternative hypotheses, and using a significance level of 10%, determine whether or not the results indicate a difference between the mean lifetimes of brand A and brand B bulbs. (6)

8. (1997), A3) A trading standards officer claims that the contents of bottles of a certain wine have a mean less than the nominal 75 cl. He therefore measures the contents, x cl, of each 100 randomly chosen bottles and obtains the following results:

$$\Sigma x = 7489, \quad \Sigma x^2 = 560863$$

(a) Calculate unbiased estimates of the mean and the variance of the contents of bottles of this wine. (3)

(b) State appropriate null and alternative hypotheses for testing the official's claim. (1)

(c) (i) Assuming that the contents are normally distributed, calculate an approximation for the p-value of the above results. (5)

9. (1997, S2) The following table gives a summary of the results obtained in an investigation of the heights (in inches) of wheat stalks grown using two fertilisers A and B.

(a) Calulate unbiased estimates of the mean and the variance of the heights of stalks grown using Fertiliser A. (2)

(b) Calculate an approximate 98% confidence interval for the mean height of stalks grown using fertiliser A. (3)

(c) From the data in the above table the unbiased estimates of the mean and the variance of the heights of stalks grown using Fertiliser B˙ are 14.9 and 5.6, respectively. Use a 5% significance level to test whether the mean heights of stalks are equal for the two fertilisers. (6)

10. (1998, A3) An ornithologist put forward the theory that, for a certain species of bird, female brids are, on average, heavier than male birds. She caught and weighed six female and five male birds, obtaining the following results:

Weights of female birds (kg) : 4.62, 5.05, 4.93, 4.82, 5.21, 4.58

Weights of male birds (kg) : 4.43, 4.95, 4.80, 5.02, 4.50

Assuming that the weights of female birds and the weights of male birds are each normally distributed with standard deviation 0.2 kg and using a 5% significance level, determine whether or not the data support the ornithologist's theory. (6)

11. (1998, S2) Two methods, A and B, are to be compared to determine which (if either) is the quicker for performing a particular task. Method A was used by each of 75 persons and the times (x minutes) they took to complete the task were such that

$$\Sigma x = 984.0 \quad \text{and} \quad \Sigma x^2 = 1353390$$

Method B was used by each of 80 persons and their times (y minutes) were such that:

$$\Sigma y = 1141.6 \quad \text{and} \quad \Sigma y^2 = 16806.50$$

Determine an approximation of the p-value when testing the equality of the mean times for completing the task. State, giving a reason, which (if either) of the two methods you would regard as being the faster on average. (10)

Chapter 5

Linear Relationships

Introduction

Consider two (non-random) variables x and y which are known to be linearly related. We shall express such a relationship in the form

$$y = \alpha + \beta x.$$

The graph of this relationship will be a straight line having intercept α with the y-axis and slope β, which is positive if y increases with x and negative if y decreases as x increases. Many of the relationships that arise in various scientific studies are often linear or may be transformed into linear form, some examples of which are as follows.

1. When an elastic string of natural length α cm is subjected to a tension of x N, its length y cm is given by $y = \alpha + \beta x$, where β is the coefficient of elasticity.

2. If a body moving in a straight line with acceleration a has initial speed u, then after time t its speed v is given by $v = u + at$, and after travelling a distance s its speed is given by $v^2 = u^2 + 2as$.

3. The period of oscillation of a simple pendulum of length L is $T = 2\pi\sqrt{(L/g)}$, where g is the acceleration due to gravity.

4. The volume v of a gas subjected to a pressure p is such that $pv^\gamma = c$, where c is a constant and γ is the specific heat of the gas.

When α and β are unknown their values can be determined uniquely given any two pairs of values (x_1, y_1) and (x_2, y_2) that satisfy the equation. However, in many practical situations, the values of x and y have to determined experimentally and there may be no guarantee that the observed values are correct. In this text we restrict consideration to the situation where the x-values can be determined accurately (or, as is often the case, are set at specific values), but the y-values are subject to experimental or measurement error. Then observed values (x, y), when plotted on a graph, will not fall on a straight line. If y_1 is the observed value of y when $x = x_1$ then we may write

$$y_1 = \alpha + \beta x_1 + \text{an error.}$$

Figure 5.1 illustrates what one may have after plotting several pairs of observed values of (x, y) even though the variables are linearly related. One may fit by eye a straight line to the plotted points as an estimate of the true linear relationship connecting x and y. Such an approach has two major disadvantages, namely

(1) being subjective, different persons will fit different straight lines,

(2) it does not enable us to make a quantitative assessment of how close the fitted line is to the true line.

One way of overcoming these disadvantages is that known as **the method of least squares**.

5.1 The method of least squares

Let (x_i, y_i), for $i = 1, 2, \ldots, n$, denote n pairs of observed values of (x, y), where it is known that $y = \alpha + \beta x$, but because an observation of y is subject to error,

$$y_i = \alpha + \beta x_i + e_i, \quad i = 1, 2, \ldots, n, \tag{1}$$

where e_i is the actual error in the observed value of y when $x = x_i$. Having plotted the points (x_i, y_i) on a graph, as in Figure 5.2, we draw a line which we feel is a reasonable fit to the plotted points. Let the equation of this fitted line be

$$y = a + bx. \tag{2}$$

For any x_i, the discrepancy between the observed y_i and the corresponding value on the fitted line is

$$d_i = y_i - (a + bx_i), \tag{3}$$

as shown in Figure 5.2. A drawn line will be a good fit if these discrepancies are small.

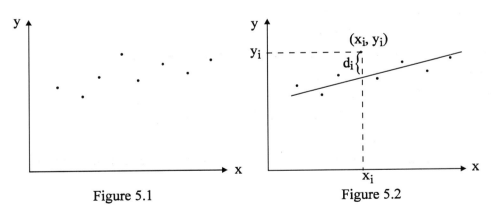

Figure 5.1   Figure 5.2

The principle used in the method of least squares is to choose a and b so that the **sum of the squares of these discrepancies is a minimum.** Thus, a and b are chosen so as to minimise

$$S = \Sigma d_i^2 = \Sigma(y_i - a - bx_i)^2 \tag{4}$$

[Throughout this chapter we shall be using Σ to denote summation over $i = 1, 2, \ldots, n$.]

Treating b as fixed, the value of a which will minimise (4) is the solution of the equation dS/da = 0. Differentiating (4) with respect to a we have

$$\frac{dS}{da} \;=\; \Sigma[-\,2(y_i - a - bx_i)] \;=\; -\,2[\Sigma y_i - na - b\Sigma x_i],$$

which is equal to zero when

$$a \;=\; (\Sigma y_i - b\Sigma x_i)/n \;\equiv\; \overline{y} - b\overline{x}, \tag{5}$$

where $\overline{x}$ and $\overline{y}$ are the means of the observed x-values and y-values, respectively. Since $d^2S/da^2 = 2n$ is positive the solution (5) is one that minimises S. It follows that, since $\overline{y} = a + b\overline{x}$, **the method of least squares gives a fitted line that passes through the mean $(\overline{x}, \overline{y})$ of the observations.**

Substituting (5) in (4) gives

$$S \;=\; \Sigma[(y_i - \overline{y}) - b(x_i - \overline{x})]^2$$

Differentiating this with respect to b gives

$$\frac{dS}{db} \;=\; -\,2\,\Sigma(x_i - \overline{x})[(y_i - \overline{y}) - b(x_i - \overline{x})]$$

$$=\; -\,2\,[\Sigma(x_i - \overline{x})(y_i - \overline{y}) - b\Sigma(x_i - \overline{x})^2]$$

which is zero when

$$b \;=\; \frac{\Sigma(x_i - \overline{x})(y_i - \overline{y})}{\Sigma(x_i - \overline{x})^2} \tag{6}$$

Since $d^2S/db^2 = 2\Sigma(x_i - \overline{x})^2$ is clearly positive, the value of b given by (6) is one for which S is a minimum. The values a and b given by (5) and (6) are referred to as the **least squares estimates of α and** β, respectively, and the straight line

$$y \;=\; a + bx \;\equiv\; \overline{y} + b(x - \overline{x}) \tag{7}$$

as the **least squares estimate** of the true linear relationship $y = \alpha + \beta x$.

In the notation of the Information Booklet,

$$b \;=\; S_{xy}/S_{xx}, \tag{8}$$

where
$$S_{xy} \;=\; \Sigma(x_i - \overline{x})(y_i - \overline{y}) \;\equiv\; \Sigma x_i y_i - (\Sigma x_i)(\Sigma y_i)/n \tag{9}$$

and
$$S_{xx} \;=\; \Sigma(x_i - \overline{x})^2 \;\equiv\; \Sigma x_i^2 - (\Sigma x_i)^2/n, \tag{10}$$

the expressions on the right being the more convenient ones when calculating a and b.

Example

The length y cm of a metal rod at a temperature of x°C is given by $y = \alpha + \beta x$. The length of the rod was measured at varying temperatures, the results obtained being as shown in the following table.

Temperature (x°C)	20	40	60	80	100
Length (y cm)	10.0	10.2	10.3	10.6	10.7

Assuming that the temperature levels are accurate and that the measured lengths are subject to error, find the least squares estimate of the relationship connecting y with x. Deduce the least squares estimate of (a) the length of the rod when the temperature is 70°C, (b) the extension in the length of the rod when the temperature is increased from 70°C to 100°C.

Solution

From the observed values of (x, y) we find

$$\Sigma x = 300, \ \Sigma x^2 = 22000, \ \Sigma y = 51.8, \text{ and } \Sigma xy = 3144.$$

Using (9) and (10,

$$S_{xy} = 3144 - (300 \times 51.8/5) = 36,$$

and $\quad S_{xx} = 22000 - 300^2/5 = 4000.$

Hence, from (8) the least squares estimate of β is

$$b = 36/4000 = 0.009.$$

Since $\bar{x} = 300/5 = 60$ and $\bar{y} = 51.8/5 = 10.36$, it follows from (7) that the least squares estimate of $y = \alpha + \beta x$ is

$$y = 10.36 + 0.009(x - 60) = 9.82 + 0.009x.$$

The observed values of (x, y) and the above straight line are shown in Figure 5.3. Such a diagram is worth drawing since it will show up any gross error that may have been made in the calculations leading to a line which is obviously inconsistent with the plotted points.

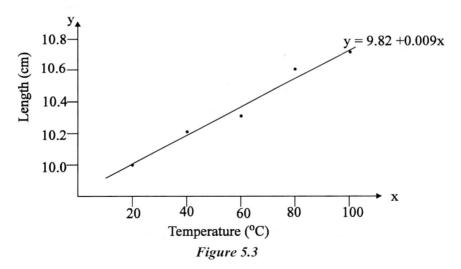

Figure 5.3

(a) Setting x = 70 in the fitted equation, the least squares estimate of the length of the rod when the temperature is 70°C is

$$y = 9.82 + 0.009 \times 70 = 10.45 \text{ cm}$$

(b) The actual extension in the length of the rod when the temperature is increased from 70°C to 100°C is given by

$$(\alpha + 100\beta) - (\alpha + 70\beta) \equiv 30\,\beta.$$

Since the least squares estimate of β is $b = 0.009$, the least squares estimate of the extension in the length of the rod is $30b = 0.27$ cm.

Exercise 5.1

Keep your solutions to the following questions as they will be required in the next exercise.

1. An experiment was performed to determine the relationship between the chemical content of a particular constituent (y grams per litre) in solution and the crystallisation temperature (x kelvin). The results obtained are shown in the following table.

x	0.3	0.4	1.2	2.3	3.1	4.2	5.3
y	3.2	3.7	4.3	5.4	6.6	7.8	8.8

It may be assumed that $y = \alpha + \beta x$, where α and β are unknown.

(a) By studying the entries in the table state whether β is positive or negative.

(b) Calculate the least square estimates of α and β, giving each value correct to three significant figures.

(c) Calculate the least squares estimate of the chemical content when the crystallisation temperature is 2.5 kelvin.

2. The length y of an elastic string is given in terms of its tension x by the formula $y = \alpha + \beta x$, where α and β are constants. Measurements of x can be made accurately but measurements of y are subject to error. The following measurements were made.

x (newtons)	5.0	7.5	10.0	12.5	15.0
y (metres)	1.23	1.39	1.52	1.66	1.81

Find the least squares estimates of α, β and the length of the string if its tension is 11.0 newtons.

3. An experiment on the solubility of a certain chemical at different temperatures gave the following results.

Temperature (x°C)	0	4	10	15	21	30	45
Measured solubility (y g)	60.2	65.1	70.3	75.2	81.2	85.1	100.2

Assuming that the solubility and the temperature can be modelled by $y = \alpha + \beta x$, find the least squares estimates of α, β and the solubility at a temperature of 25°C.

4. The weight percent, w, of nitrous oxide in a mixture of nitrous oxide and nitrous dioxide at temperature t is given by the relationship $w = \alpha + \beta t^{-1}$, where α and β are constants. In an experiment to estimate α and β, the temperature t was carefully controlled at four different values and three determinations of w were made at each temperature value. Letting $x = 1000t^{-1}$, the following calculations were made from the 12 observed values of (x, w):

$$\Sigma x = 43.2, \quad \Sigma x^2 = 161.28, \quad \Sigma w = 13.2, \quad \Sigma xw = 44.64.$$

Find the least squares estimates of α, β and the value of w when $t = 250$.

5. An investigation of a possible linear relationship between two variables x and y was conducted with x having five prespecified values, the corresponding values of y being observed. The results obtained are given in the following table.

x	5	10	15	20	25
y	55	52	50	48	45

Assuming that the true relationship between x and y is $y = \alpha + \beta x$, determine the least squares estimates of (a) α, (b) β, (c) the true value of y when $x = 20$, (d) the difference between the true values of y when $x = 5$ and when $x = 25$.

6. It is known that the response y in a certain chemical experiment is a linear function of the operating temperature x. However, the experimental determinations of y are subject to error. The following table gives the observed responses in six experiments, two at each of three temperatures.

	Temperature (x)		
	30	40	50
Observed responses	14	10	7
	12	11	6

Determine the least squares estimate of the linear relationship expressing y in terms of x. Deduce an estimate of the true change in the response when the operating temperature is increased from 30 to 45.

7. It is known that the heart rate of a patient treated with a certain drug is linearly related to the dose administered, the precise form of the linear relationship being dependent on the patient. The following table shows the heart rate, y beats per minute, of a patient treated with x grains of the drug on five distinct occasions.

Dose (x grains)	1	2	3	4	5
Heart rate (y beats per minute)	52	63	75	89	101

For this patient, calculate the least squares estimate of (a) the linear relationship between y and x, (b) the increase in the heart rate corresponding to an increase of 1 grain in the dose of the drug.

5.2 Inference

How good are the least squares estimates? To answer this question we need to make some distributional assumptions. Recall from the Introduction that we are assuming that the variables x and y are related in the form $y = \alpha + \beta x$ and that, whereas observed values of x are accurate, the corresponding observed values of y are subject to experimental or measurement error. Thus, when $x = x_i$ the observed value of y is

$$y_i = \alpha + \beta x_i + e_i,$$

where e_i is the error in the observed y-value. We shall assume that **the e_i are independent observations of a random variable E which is normally distributed with mean zero and known standard deviation σ.** Thus, y_i may be regarded as a random observation of the random variable

$$Y_i = \alpha + \beta x_i + E.$$

Since $\alpha + \beta x_i$ is a constant and $E \sim N(0, \sigma^2)$ it follows from the properties of normal distributions covered in Section 1.6 of S2, that $Y_i \sim N(\alpha + \beta x_i, \sigma^2)$.

The quantities about which we may wish to make inferences (as confidence limits or testing hypotheses) are (a) α, (b) β, and (c) $y_0 = \alpha + \beta x_0$ for some specified x_0. Denote the corresponding estimators by (a) A, (b) B, and (c) $Y_0 = A + Bx_0$, respectively. Then, as will be shown in Section 5.3, under the assumptions made above the sampling distributions of these estimators are as follows (and are given in the Information Booklet):

$$A \sim N\left(\alpha, \frac{\sigma^2 \Sigma x_i^2}{n S_{xx}}\right) \tag{1}$$

$$B \sim N\left(\beta, \frac{\sigma^2}{S_{xx}}\right) \tag{2}$$

$$Y_0 \sim N\left(\alpha + \beta x_0, \sigma^2\left[\frac{1}{n} + \frac{(x_0 - \bar{x})^2}{S_{xx}}\right]\right) \tag{3}$$

[An alternative expression for Var(A) can be obtained by putting $x_0 = 0$ in Var(Y_0).]

Note, in particular, that each estimator is unbiased and has a known standard error (since σ is assumed to be known). Note further that the standard error of Y_0 increases with $|x_0 - \bar{x}|$, so that the estimate of the true value of y for a specified value of x becomes less reliable the further away that value of x is from $\bar{x}$.

Finding confidence limits or testing hypotheses for any one of α, β, and $\alpha + \beta x_0$ will be obvious modifications of the corresponding inferences made on the mean μ of a normal distribution based on the observed mean of a random sample of observations from the distribution. Let W denote an arbitrary one of A, B and Y_0. Denoting the mean of W by μ_w, then

$$Z \equiv \frac{W - \mu_w}{SE(W)} \sim N(0, 1).$$

Following the procedure we used in Section 3.1 the $100(1 - 2\alpha)\%$ confidence limits for μ_w are

$$w \pm z_\alpha SE(W) \tag{4}$$

where w is the observed value of W and z_α is such that $P(Z > z_\alpha) = \alpha$.

Similarly, following the procedure in Section 4.1.1, the p-values when testing $H_0 : \mu_w = \mu_0$ are as follows.

(i) For testing $H_0 : \mu_w = \mu_0$ against $H_1 : \mu_w > \mu_0$,

$$\text{the p-value} = P(W \geq w \text{ when } H_0 \text{ is true}). \tag{5}$$

(ii) For testing $H_0 : \mu_w = \mu_0$ against $H_1 : \mu_w < \mu_0$,

$$\text{the p-value} = P(W \leq w \text{ when } H_0 \text{ is true}). \tag{6}$$

(iii) For testing $H_0 : \mu_w = \mu_0$ against $H_1 : \mu_w \neq \mu_0$,

$$\text{if } w > \mu_0 \text{ the p-value} = 2P(W \geq w \text{ when } H_0 \text{ is true}) \tag{7a}$$

$$\text{if } w < \mu_0 \text{ the p-value} = 2P(W \leq w \text{ when } H_0 \text{ is true}) \tag{7b}$$

The following example illustrates the procedures for finding confidence limits and for testing a hypothesis.

Example

The length y cm of a metal rod at a temperature of $x°C$ is given by $y = \alpha + \beta x$. The length of the rod was measured at varying temperatures, the results obtained being as shown in the following table. Assume that the temperature levels were accurate and that the measured lengths were subject to error.

Temperature (x°C)	20	40	60	80	100
Length (y cm)	10.0	10.2	10.3	10.6	10.7

(a) Find the least squares estimates of α and β.

Assume further that the errors in the measured lengths are independent and normally distributed with mean zero and standard deviation 0.1.

(b) Calculate 95% confidence limits for (i) the length of the rod when the temperature is 70°C, (ii) the extension in the length of the rod when the temperature is increased from 70°C to 100°C.

(c) Using a 5% significance level, test $H_0 : \beta = 0.012$ against $H_1 : \beta < 0.012$.

(d) The same experiment was conducted with another metal rod, the temperature being as given in the above table. Assume that for this rod its length y cm at temperature x°C is given by $y = \alpha' + \beta'x$. From the results of this experiment the least squares estimate of β' was found to be b' = 0.005. Using a 10% significance level test the hypothesis $H_0 : \beta = \beta'$ against the alternative $H_1 : \beta \neq \beta'$.

Solution

(a) In the example of Section 5.1 we showed that the least squares estimates of α and β were a = 9.82 and b = 0.009, respectively.

(b)(i) The true length of the rod when the temperature is 70°C is $\alpha + 70\beta$, the least squares estimate of which is

$$y_0 = 9.82 + 70 \times 0.009 = 10.45.$$

The corresponding least square estimator is Y_0 whose distribution is given by (3) above. Thus, since n = 5, x_0 = 70, $\bar{x}$ = 60, S_{xx} = 4000, and σ = 0.1,

$$SE(Y_0) = \sqrt{0.1^2\left[\frac{1}{5} + \frac{(70-60)^2}{4000}\right]} = 0.0474.$$

It follows from (4) that the 95% confidence limits for the true value of y when x = 70 are:

$$y_0 \pm 1.96 \, SE\,(Y_0) = 10.45 \pm 1.96 \times 0.0474 = 10.36 \text{ and } 10.54.$$

(c) Since b = 0.009 it follows from (6) that for testing H_0: $\beta = 0.012$ against H_1: $\beta < 0.012$,

the p-value = $P(B \leq 0.009$ when $\beta = 0.012)$

From (2) $SE(B) = \sqrt{0.1^2 / 4000} \approx 0.001581.$

Hence   the p-value = $P\left(Z \leq \dfrac{0.009 - 0.012}{0.001581}\right) \cong P(Z \leq -1.90) = 0.029.$

Since the significance level of 0.05 is greater than the p-value the decision is to reject H_0 and conclude that $\beta < 0.012$. [Alternatively, one could have used the critical z method.]

(d) An appropriate statistic for testing $H_0 : \beta = \beta'$ is B – B', where B and B' are the least square estimators of β and β', respectively. It is clear that B and B' are independent since two distinct experiments have been performed. Hence

$$SE(B - B') = \sqrt{Var(B) + Var(B')}.$$

Since the same x-values were used in the two experiments, it follows from (2) that
$$\text{Var}(B) = \text{Var}(B') = 0.1^2/4000,$$

and therefore, $\quad \text{SE}(B - B') = \sqrt{\dfrac{2 \times 0.1^2}{4000}} = 0.002236.$

Furthermore, since B and B' are normally distributed so is B − B' normally distributed, its mean being $\beta - \beta'$. The observed values of B and B' were b = 0.009 and b' = 0.005. Thus, using (7a),

$$\text{the p-value} = 2P(B - B' \geq 0.009 - 0.005 \text{ when } \beta = \beta')$$

$$= 2P\left(Z \geq \frac{0.004 - 0}{0.002236} \right) \cong 2P(Z \geq 1.79)$$

$$= 2 \times 0.0367 = 0.073$$

Since the significance level of 0.1 exceeds this p-value we reject H_0 and conclude that $\beta > \beta'$ (since b > b'). This means that the extension in length per 1°C increase in temperature for the first rod is greater than that for the second rod.

[Alternatively, we could have answered this part by either finding the decision rule having significance level 0.1 or by finding the 90% confidence interval for $\beta - \beta'$.]

Exercise 5.2

1. In Question 1 of Exercise 5.1 suppose that the y-determinations are subject to independent random errors each having mean zero and standard deviation 0.5 grams per litre.

(a) Determine 95% confidence limits for α. State the conclusion to be drawn if a significance level of 0.05 is used to test $H_0 : \alpha = 2.5$ against $H_1 : \alpha \neq 2.5$.

(b) Use a 5% significance level to test the null hypothesis that the true value of y when x = 2.5 is 5.3 against the alternative hypothesis that it is > 5.3.

2. In Question 2 of Exercise 5.1 the measured lengths were subject to errors which are independent and normally distributed with mean zero and standard deviation 0.008 m.

(a) Calculate 95% confidence limits for the unstretched length of the string.

(b) Let y_0 m be the length of the string when the tension is 11 Newtons. Find the p-value when testing $H_0 : y_0 = 1.59$ against $H_1 : y_0 < 1.59$. State the conclusion to be drawn if the significance level is 0.01.

3. In Question 3 of Exercise 5.1 the measured solubilities were subject to random errors which are normally distributed with mean zero and standard deviation 1.5 g.

Calculate 95% confidence limits for the solubility when the temperature is 25°C.

4. In Question 4 of Exercise 5.1 the observed values of w were subject to independent normally distributed errors having mean zero and standard deviation 0.08.

(a) Calculate 95% confidence limits for β.

(b) When $t = 250$ test, at the 5% significance level, the null hypothesis that the true value of w is equal to 1 against the alternative hypothesis that it is less than 1.

5.   In Question 5 of Exercise 5.1 the determinations of y were subject to normally distributed errors having mean zero and standard deviation 0.5.

Calculate 90% confidence limits for (a) the true value of y when $x = 20$, (b) the change in the value of y when x is increased from 5 to 25.

6. In Question 6 of Exercise 5.1 the observed responses were subject to errors which are normally distributed with mean zero and standard deviation 0.1.

Calculate 90% confidence limits for the change in the value of y when the temperature is increased by 15 units.

7.   In Question 7 of Exercise 5.1 the measured heart rates were subject to normally distributed errors having mean zero and standard deviation 0.5 beats per minute.

(a) Calculate 90% confidence limits for β, the increase in the heart rate of this patient per 1 gram increase in the dose of the drug.

(b)   The same experiment was conducted on another patient using the same dosages of the drug (as given in the table).   From the results of this experiment the least squares estimate of β', the increase in the heart rate per 1 gram increase in the dose of the drug was 10.9.   Calculate 95% confidence limits for $\beta - \beta'$.

The following question is concerned with the application of the method of least squares to the simpler linear model $y = \beta x$.   Answering this question will help in the understanding of the derivations given in Section 5.3 of the sampling distributions given above.

8.   Corresponding to a given value of x_i of a variable x there is a random variable Y_i which is normally distributed with mean βx_i and standard deviation σ.   Let $y_1, y_2, \ldots, y_n$ denote the observed values of Y_i when $x = x_i$ for $i = 1, 2, \ldots, n$.

Apply the method of least squares to this model to show that the least squares estimate of β is $b = (\Sigma x_i y_i)/(\Sigma x_i^2)$.   Verify that b is an unbiased estimate of β and show that its standard error is $\sigma / \sqrt{\Sigma x_i^2}$.

Calculate the value of b given the following set of values of (x_i, y_i).

x_i	2	4	6	8
y_i	3.1	6.5	9.5	13.0

Given that $\sigma = 0.3$, calculate a 95% confidence interval for β and deduce a 95% confidence interval for the true value of y when $x = 5$.

5.3 Derivation of the sampling distributions

We shall show that each of the least square estimators of α, β and $\alpha + \beta x_0$ can be expressed in the form $\Sigma c_i Y_i$, where the c_i are constants and, as indicated in Section 5.2, the Y_i are independent and normally distributed with mean $\alpha + \beta x_i$ and variance σ^2. Using the result that a linear combination of independent normally distributed random variables is also normally distributed (see Section 2.4 of the S2 book), it follows that $\Sigma c_i Y_i$ is normally distributed with mean $\Sigma c_i E(Y_i)$ and variance $\sigma^2 \Sigma c_i^2$.

(a) Sampling distribution of B

From Section 5.1, the least squares estimate of β is

$$b = S_{xy}/S_{xx},$$

where $S_{xy} = \Sigma(x_i - \bar{x})(y_i - \bar{y}) \equiv \Sigma(x_i - \bar{x})y_i - \bar{y}\Sigma(x_i - \bar{x}) = \Sigma(x_i - \bar{x})y_i,$

since $\Sigma(x_i - \bar{x}) = 0$. Hence, the least squares estimator of β may be written as

$$B = \Sigma(x_i - \bar{x})Y_i/S_{xx}. \tag{1}$$

The mean of B is

$$
\begin{aligned}
E(B) &= \Sigma(x_i - \bar{x})E(Y_i)/S_{xx} = \Sigma(x_i - \bar{x})(\alpha + \beta x_i)/S_{xx} \\
&= [\alpha\Sigma(x_i - \bar{x}) + \beta\Sigma x_i(x_i - \bar{x})]/S_{xx} = [\beta\Sigma x_i(x_i - \bar{x})]/S_{xx}
\end{aligned}
$$

Now $S_{xx} = \Sigma(x_i - \bar{x})^2 \equiv \Sigma x_i(x_i - \bar{x}) - \bar{x}\Sigma(x_i - \bar{x}) = \Sigma x_i(x_i - \bar{x})$

and, therefore, $E(B) = \beta,$

which establishes that B is an unbiased estimator of β.

Since the Y_i are independent and each has variance σ^2, it follows from (1) that

$$\text{Var}(B) = \Sigma(x_i - \bar{x})^2\sigma^2/S_{xx}^2 = \sigma^2 S_{xx}/S_{xx}^2 = \sigma^2/S_{xx}$$

Thus the sampling distribution of B is normal with mean β and standard error $\sigma/\sqrt{S_{xx}}$, as given in Section 5.2.

(b) The sampling distribution of A

From Section 5.1, the least squares estimate of α is $a = \bar{y} - b\bar{x}$, so that the least squares estimator of α is

$$A = \bar{Y} - B\bar{x}. \tag{2}$$

The mean of A is

$$E(A) = E(\bar{Y}) - \bar{x}E(B).$$

But $E(\bar{Y}) = \dfrac{1}{n}\Sigma E(Y_i) = \dfrac{1}{n}\Sigma(\alpha + \beta x_i) = \alpha + \beta\bar{x}$ and $E(B) = \beta.$

Hence $E(A) = (\alpha + \beta\bar{x}) - \bar{x}\beta = \alpha,$

which establishes that A is an unbiased estimator of α. Unless we first prove that $\overline{Y}$ and B are independent, (2) is not suitable for finding Var(A). To find Var(A) we shall convert (2) into the form $\Sigma c_i Y_i$. From (2) we immediately have

$$A \;=\; \frac{1}{n}\Sigma Y_i - \overline{x}\,\frac{\Sigma(x_i - \overline{x})Y_i}{S_{xx}} \;\equiv\; \Sigma\left[\frac{1}{n} - \frac{\overline{x}(x_i - \overline{x})}{S_{xx}}\right]Y_i \qquad (3)$$

Hence

$$Var(A) \;=\; \Sigma\left[\frac{1}{n^2} - \frac{2\overline{x}(x_i - \overline{x})}{nS_{xx}} + \frac{\overline{x}^2(x_i - \overline{x})^2}{S_{xx}^{\,2}}\right]\sigma^2$$

$$=\; \sigma^2\left[\frac{1}{n} + \frac{\overline{x}^2}{S_{xx}}\right], \;\text{ since } \Sigma(x_i - \overline{x}) = 0 \text{ and } \Sigma(x_i - \overline{x})^2 = S_{xx}$$

$$=\; \sigma^2[S_{xx} + n\overline{x}^2]/nS_{xx} \;=\; \sigma^2\Sigma x_i^2/nS_{xx},$$

on noting that $S_{xx} = \Sigma x_i^2 - n\overline{x}^2$. Hence, the sampling distribution of A is normal with mean α and standard error $\sigma\sqrt{\Sigma x_i^2/nS_{xx}}$ as given in Section 5.2.

(c) The sampling distribution of $Y_0 = A + Bx_0$

The mean of Y_0 is

$$E(Y_0) \;=\; E(A) + x_0 E(B) \;=\; \alpha + \beta x_0,$$

which shows that Y_0 is an unbiased estimator of the true value of y when $x = x_0$. Substituting the expressions for A and B given in (1) and (3) we have

$$Y_0 \;=\; \Sigma\left[\frac{1}{n} - \frac{\overline{x}(x_i - \overline{x})}{S_{xx}} + \frac{x_0(x_i - \overline{x})}{S_{xx}}\right]Y_i \;\equiv\; \Sigma\left[\frac{1}{n} + \frac{(x_0 - \overline{x})(x_i - \overline{x})}{S_{xx}}\right]Y_i$$

$$\text{Thus } Var(Y_0) = \Sigma\left[\frac{1}{n^2} + \frac{2(x_0 - \overline{x})(x_i - \overline{x})}{2nS_{xx}} + \frac{(x_0 - \overline{x})^2(x_i - \overline{x})^2}{S_{xx}^{\,2}}\right]\sigma^2$$

$$=\; \sigma^2\left[\frac{1}{n} + \frac{(x_0 - \overline{x})^2}{S_{xx}}\right], \;\text{ on noting that } \Sigma(x_i - \overline{x}) = 0,$$

as stated in Section 5.2.

Exercise 5.3

1. Two variables are known to be such that $y = \alpha + \beta x$ for all $0 \le x \le a$, where α and β are unknown constants. Experimental observations of the values of y corresponding to fixed values of x are subject to independent random errors that are normally distributed with mean zero and standard deviation σ. In order to estimate β it is decided to carry out a total of 2n experiments with x fixed at values $x_1, x_2, \ldots, x_{2n}$, respectively, and to observe the corresponding values of y. By comparing standard errors, determine which of the following two sets of 2n values of x is the better one to use for estimating β.

Set 1 : $x_1 = x_2 = \ldots = x_n = 0$, $x_{n+1} = x_{n+2} = \ldots = x_{2n} = a$.

Set 2 : $x_i = [(i-1)a]/(2n-1)$ for $i = 1, 2, \ldots, 2n$.

2. Two variables x and y are such that $y = \alpha + \beta x$, where α and β are unknown constants. Experiments were conducted with x taking the values $1, 2, \ldots, 2n$, respectively, and the corresponding values of y were measured to be $y_1, y_2, \ldots, y_{2n}$. Assuming that the y-measurements are subject to independent random errors having mean zero and standard deviation σ, show that

$$b' = \frac{1}{n^2}\left\{\sum_{i=n+1}^{2n} y_i - \sum_{i=1}^{n} y_i\right\}$$

is an unbiased estimate of β but has a larger standard error than the least squares estimate of β.

Miscellaneous Questions on Chapter 5

[Note that hypothesis testing was not examined by the WJEC prior to 1996.]

1. (1987) In an investigation of the relationship $y = \alpha + \beta x$ connecting two variables x and y, five experiments were conducted with x having the values 20, 30, 40, 50, and 60, respectively, and the corresponding values of y were measured. The least squares estimate of the relationship was calculated from the results to be $y = 3.4 - 0.65x$. Assuming that the errors in the y-measurements are independent and normally distributed with mean zero and standard deviation 0.2, calculate 90% confidence limits for the values of (i) α, (ii) β. (7)

2. (1988) It is known that the true response, y, in a certain chemical process is linearly related to the operating temperature $x°C$. However, experimental determinations of y are subject to random errors so that when the process is run at temperature $x_i°C$ the observed response is given by $y_i = \alpha + \beta x_i + e_i$, where $\alpha + \beta x_i$ is the true response and e_i is the error. The following table gives the responses that were observed in nine runs, three at each of the temperatures 20°C, 30°C, and 40°C.

	Temperature		
	20	30	40
Observed	35	31	28
responses (y_i)	33	32	27
	34	31	29

(i) Calculate the least square estimates of α and β. (You are given that $\Sigma x_i y_i = 8220$.)

(ii) The errors, e_i, are independent and normally distributed with mean zero and standard deviation 2.5. Calculate 95% confidence intervals for (a) the value of β, (b) the true value of y when x = 40.

(iii) Explain why the confidence interval you calculated in (ii)(b) is preferable to the one that could be obtained from the three observed responses when x = 40. (15)

3. (1989) A fixed length of steel wire was subjected to forces of 300, 400, 500 and 700 Newtons, respectively. The measured lengths, in cm, of the stretched wire are shown in the following table. It may be assumed that the errors in the measured lengths are independent and normally distributed with mean zero and standard deviation 0.01 cm.

Force (x N)	300	400	500	600	700
Length (y cm)	10.35	10.46	10.58	10.71	10.80

You are given that $\Sigma y = 52.9$ and $\Sigma xy = 26565$.

According to Hooke's law, when a wire of natural length α cm is subjected to a force of x Newtons its stretched length, y cm, is given by $y = \alpha + \beta x$, where β is a constant dependent upon some properties of the wire.

(a) Calculate the least squares estimates of α and β.

(b) Calculate 95% confidence limits for (i) the natural length of the wire, (ii) the stretched length of the wire when it is subjected to a force of 555 newtons. (15)

4. (1990) A physical law states that the variables x and y are linearly related in the form $y = \alpha + \beta x$. To verify this relationship experiments were conducted with x having prespecified values and the corresponding values of y were measured. It is known that the measured values of y are subject to independent random errors that are normally distributed with mean zero and standard deviation 0.06. The results of the experiments are shown in the following table.

x	2.0	2.5	3.0	3.5
Measured y	10.8	9.5	8.4	7.3

The experimenter used a calculator to determine the least squares estimate of the relation and produced the equation $y = 2.3 + 2.4x$.

(i) Without performing any calculations state why it is clear from the data that the experimenter's equation is incorrect.

(ii) Calculate the correct least squares estimate of the relation.

(iii) Calculate 95% confidence limits for β.

(iv) The law referred to above is actually valid only when the experiments are conducted at a fixed constant temperature. In another series of experiments to verify the relation the same values of x were used but the temperature was held constant at a different value from that in the first series of experiments. The results obtained in this second series of experiments led to the least squares estimate of the relation being $y = 17.6 - 1.96x$. Assuming that the errors in the measured values of y from the second series of experiments have the same distribution as those in first series, calculate 95% confidence limits for the difference, at the two temperature levels, between the true values of y when $x = 3$. (15)

5. (1991) The variables x and y are known to be linearly related. Experiments were conducted with x having ten prespecified values, the corresponding values of y being measured. The results (x_i, y_i), $i = 1, 2, \ldots, 10$ of the experiments were summarised as follows :

$$\Sigma x_i = 80, \quad \Sigma x_i^2 = 3140, \quad \Sigma y_i = 422, \quad \Sigma x_i y_i = 12276$$

The y-measurements were subject to independent normally distributed errors having mean zero and standard deviation 2.4.

Find (i) the least squares estimate of the equation expressing y in terms of x,

(ii) 95% confidence limits for the increase that will occur in the value of y when x is increased by one unit. (7)

6. (1992) Two variables x and y are known to be related in the form $y = \alpha + \beta x$. To investigate this relationship four experiments were conducted with x having the values 10, 20, 30 and 40, respectively. The corresponding values of y were then measured. A measured value of y is a random observation from a normal distribution having mean equal to the true value of y and standard deviation 1.2. On applying the method of least squares to the experimental results the estimated relationship was $y = 8.4 + 2.6x$.

(i) Find the mean of the four measured values of y.

(ii) Calculate a 95% confidence interval for the value of β. (6)

7. (1993) In enzyme chemistry x and y are two variables such that

$$y = \frac{1}{M} + \frac{K}{M}x,$$

where M and K are constants. In a particular experiment the following data on x and y were obtained.

x	0.6	1.0	2.0	3.5	4.5	7.0
y	2.0	2.4	3.2	4.4	5.8	6.7

(a) Find, correct to two decimal places, the values of a and b if y = a + bx is the least squares estimate of the equation expressing y in terms of x. Hence obtain estimates of M and K. (8)

(b) Given that the errors in the y-values are independent and normally distributed with mean zero and standard deviation 0.4, determine 95% confidence limits for M. (7)

8. (1994) The length y mm of a wire is related to its temperature x°C by the equation y = α + βx. The values of x can be pre-determined and the measured values of y are subject to independent normally distributed random errors with mean zero and standard deviation 0.2 mm.

The following results were obtained for a particular wire.

Temperature °C	10	15	20	25	30	35
Measured length mm	143.6	145.3	146.7	148.2	150.2	151.5

(a) Calculate the least squares estimates of α, β. Give your answers correct to four significant figures. (6)

(b) Calculate 99% confidence limits for (i) the value of β, (ii) the true length of the wire at 30°C. (8)

(c) At what temperature can the length be estimated most precisely using the above data? (1)

9. (1995) The variables x and y are related by the equation y = α + βx, where α, β are unknown constants. Eight pairs of observations $(x_1, y_1), (x_2, y_2), \ldots, (x_8, y_8)$ gave the following results.

$$\Sigma x_i = 36, \quad \Sigma x_i^2 = 204, \quad \Sigma y_i = 76.21, \quad \Sigma x_i y_i = 396.32.$$

(a) Calculate the least squares estimate of α and β, giving your answers correct to 3 significant figures.

(b) Observations on x are exact and observations on y are subject to independent normally distributed errors with mean zero and standard deviation 0.2.

(i) Calculate the standard error of your estimate of β.

(ii) Calculate 95% compitence limits for β.

10. (A3 1996) When a dose (x mg) of a certain drug is given to a patient, the pulse rate (y beats per minute) can be modelled by the linear equation

$$y = α + βx$$

where the constants α, β may vary from patient to patient. Measurements of pulse rate are subject to independent random errors that are normally distributed with mean zero and standard deviation 0.4. The following table shows the measured pulse rates of a particular patient after taking various doses of the drug.

Dose (x mg)	1	2	3	4	5	6
Pulse rate (y beats per min)	50	56	64	71	78	86

(a) The following results were calculated from the above table.

$$\Sigma x = 21, \quad \Sigma y = 405, \quad \Sigma xy = 1544, \quad \Sigma x^2 = 91.$$

Use these results to determine

(i) the least squares estimates of α and β for this patient. (4)

(ii) the 95% confidence limits for the true value of y when x = 5 for this patient. (3)

(b) The same experiment was carried out independently on another patient using the same doses of the drug as in the above table. Analysis of the results gave a least squares estimate of β equal to 7.52. Test the hypothesis that the values of β for the two patients are equal, using a two-sided test with significance level 1%. (6)

11. (S2 1996) An experiment was carried out to determine the mass, y g, of a certain substance that dissolves in a litre of water at a temperature of x°C. The following results were obtained.

Temperature (x°C)	10	20	30	40	50	60
Mass (y g)	14.2	16.1	18.4	19.9	22.3	24.6

$$[\Sigma x = 210; \quad \Sigma y = 115.5; \quad \Sigma x^2 = 9100; \quad \Sigma xy = 4403]$$

(a) Assuming that x, y are related by the equation

$$y = \alpha + \beta x,$$

calculate the least squares estimates of α and β, showing all your working. (4)

(b) The temperature measurements were accurate whereas the measurements of y were subject to independent normally distributed errors with mean zero and standard deviation 0.3.

Determine 95% confidence limits for

(i) the value of β, (4)

(ii) the true value of y when x = 25. (4)

12. (A3 1997) A gardener decided to test a new fertiliser on his tomato plants. He kept a record of the amount of fertiliser applied to, and the yield obtained from, each of six plants. His results are given in the table below.

Fertiliser applied (x kg per week)	0	5	10	15	20	25
Total yield (y kg)		4.32	4.96	5.43	5.82	6.12	6.21

(a)(i) Calculate Σx, Σy, Σx^2, and Σxy.

(ii) Assuming a linear relationship $y = \alpha + \beta x$, use your values to calculate, correct to three significant figures, the least squares estimates of α and β. Show your working.

(6)

(b) Calculate a 90% confidence interval for β given hat the yields are subject to independent errors that are normally distributed with mean zero and standard deviation $\sigma = 0.05$.

(4)

(c) Plot a scatter diagram of the data. Comment briefly on the adequacy of the linear model in this situation.

(2)

13. (S2 1997) A chemist knows that a variable y associated with the output of a chemical process is linearly related to the operating temperature $x^\circ C$ in the form $y = \alpha + \beta x$. The process was run twice at each of the operating temperatures $50^\circ C$, $60^\circ C$ and $70^\circ C$ with the results given in the following table.

x	50	60	70
First observed value of y	76	63	53
Second observed value of y	75	66	57

The following calculations were made from the above six pairs of results:
$$\sum x = 360, \ \sum x^2 = 22000, \ \sum y = 390, \ \sum xy = 22990$$

(a) Find the least squares estimates of α and β.

(4)

(b) Observed values of y are subject to independent normally distributed errors having mean zero and standard deviation 1.5.

(i) Calculate 95% confidence limits for β. Deduce 95% confidence limits for the decrease in the true value of y when x is increased by $10^\circ C$.

(ii) Use a 5% significance level to test the null hypothesis that when $x = 65$ the true value of y is equal to 59 against the alternative hypothesis that it is greater than 59.

(10)

14. (A3 1998) An effluent pipe discharges water into a river. An environmental officer measures the pollution (in appropriate units) at various distances downstream from the pipe and obtains the following results.

Distance from pipe (x miles)	1	2	3	4	5
Amount of pollution (y units)	38.07	33.96	29.47	26.58	24.46

$$\sum x = 15, \ \sum y = 152 \cdot 54, \ \sum x^2 = 55, \ \sum xy = 423 \cdot 02.$$

The officer asks you to fit the linear relationship $y = \alpha + \beta x$ to these data.

(a) Calculate the least squares estimates of α and β.

(4)

(b) The x-values are exact whereas the y-values are subject to normally distributed random measurement errors with mean zero and standard deviation 0.8.

(i) Calculate 99% confidence limits for β. Hence find 99% confidence limits for the difference in pollution at two points A and B which are situated 1.5 miles and 3.2 miles, respectively, downstream from the effluent pipe.

(ii) He now wishes to estimate the pollution 4.5 miles downstream from the pipe. He considers two possible unbiased estimates.

    Estimate 1: the mean of the two values of y in the table when x = 4 and x = 5.
    Estimate 2: the value of y obtained by putting x = 4⊐5 in the linear relationship found in (a).

Calculate the values of these two estimates. Find the standard errors of these two estimates. Hence state, giving a reason, which is the better estimate.

15. (S2 1998) The length y metres of a cable subject to a load of x kilograms is given by y = α + βx. In an experiment to estimate α and β for a particular cable, the value of y was measured for each of 15 values of x. The following quantities were calculated from the 15 pairs of values.

$$\sum x = 225, \sum y = 238 \cdot 5, \sum x^2 = 3625, \sum xy = 3581$$

(a) Calculate the least squares estimates of α and β. (4)

The measured values of y were subject to independent normally distributed errors having mean zero and standard deviation 0.02 m.

(b) Assuming a 5% significance level, test the null hypothesis that β = 0.016 against the alternative hypothesis that it is less than 0.016. (4)

(c) Calculate 98% confidence limits for the length of the cable when it is subjected to a load of 20 kg. (4)

16. (A3 1999) The variables x and y are related by the equation y = α + βx, where α and β are unknown constants. In an experiment, the values of x can be set exactly whereas the measured values of y are subject to independent normally distributed random errors with mean zero and standard deviation 0.35. The experimenter set the values of x successively to 10, 20, 30, 40 and 50 and measured the five corresponding values of y. He then correctly calculated the least squares estimates of α and β to be 2.21 and 0.85, respectively.

(a) Find the mean of his five measurements. (2)

(b) Find 95% confidence limits or the true value of y when x = 35. (6)

17. (S2 1999) A researcher knows that the two variables x and y are linearly related in the form y = α + βx, where x and y are unknown constants. An experiment was conducted

with x having the values 5, 10, 15, 20 and 25, respectively, and the corresponding values of y were measured. On applying the method of least squares to the observed results the researcher's estimate of the relationship was $y = 13.4 + 0.35x$.

(a) Calculate the mean of the five observed values of y.   (2)

The measured values of y were subject to independent normally distributed errors having mean zero and standard deviation 0.3.

(b) Determine 90% confidence limits for the value of α.   (6)

(c) Prior to conducting the experiment the researcher was of the opinion that $\alpha = 14$. How should the researcher revise this value of α in the light of the result in (b)? Give a reason for your answer.   (1)

NUMERICAL ANSWERS

Exercise 1.1

1. $\dfrac{61}{225}, \dfrac{61}{600}$ **2.** $\dfrac{3}{5}$ **6.** (a) $\mu = 4, \sigma^2 = 14.4$ **7.** 46.8, 0.093^r **8.** (a) 0.8 (b) 0.4

Exercise 1.2

2. 1.38 **4.** $1\dfrac{2}{3}, \dfrac{5}{9}$; (a) $1\dfrac{2}{3}, \dfrac{5}{27}$, (b) $\dfrac{85}{54}$, (c) $\dfrac{7}{6}$

Exercise 1.3a

1. 0.8, 0.04 **2.** $2\dfrac{1}{2}, \dfrac{5}{48}$ **3.** $\dfrac{7}{12}, \dfrac{1}{144}$ **4.** 25, 375; 25, 93.75

5. 2.5, 0.5 **6.** $n = 64$

Exercise 1.3b

1. 0.9615 **2.** 0.019 **3.** 0.023 **4.** (a) 0.038 (b) 0.038 **5.** 0.997

6. 0.997 **7.** (a) 0.5 (b) 0.841 **8.** 0.118 **9.** 0.736, 32 cm **10.** 0.866

Exercise 1.4

1. 0.7, 0.0525 **2.** 0.000384 **3.** (a) $\dfrac{1}{2}, \dfrac{1}{80}$ (b) $\dfrac{1}{3}, \dfrac{1}{90}$ (c) $\dfrac{1}{6}, \dfrac{1}{144}$

4. $\dfrac{1}{64}, \dfrac{63}{40960}$ **5.** $\dfrac{5}{8}, \dfrac{1}{64}$

Miscellaneous Questions on Chapter 1

1. 0.8 **2.** $4\dfrac{2}{3}$ **3.** $\dfrac{3}{4}\alpha, \dfrac{3}{80}\alpha^2$ **4.** (a) 2.8, 0.6 (b)(ii) $\dfrac{7}{75}$ (c) 4

5. (i) 21.5, 5.25 (ii) 86, 14 (iii) 86, 21 **6.** 0.14 **9.** (b) 2.4, 0.64 (c) 0.1303

10. (b) 14.4 **11.** (c) $4\dfrac{2}{3}$ **12.** (a) $\dfrac{1}{12n}$ (c) $n = 33$

Exercise 2.1

1. T_3 **2.** $a = b = \dfrac{1}{2}$ **3.** $c = 2, \dfrac{\theta^2}{3n}$ **4.** $a = \dfrac{1}{2}, b = \dfrac{1}{4}$; 12 **5.** 1.875

6. (a) 4.98, 0.01 (b) 0.6827 **7.** $\dfrac{\theta}{\sqrt{30}}$ **8.** $c = \dfrac{2}{3}; \dfrac{1}{3}\theta$ **9.** 4.26; $\theta \geq 4.4$

Exercise 2.2

1. 0.6, 0.0693, 0.0707 **2.** 0.002, 0.014, 0.05 **3.** 0.6, 0.0354 **4.** T_2

5. $\dfrac{1}{20}\theta(1-\theta)$; $\dfrac{1}{20}\theta(1-2\theta)$; T_2 **7.** $\dfrac{(n-X)(n-X-1)}{n(n-1)}$ **9.** 0.0151

Exercise 2.3

1. 3.8, $\dfrac{1}{7}$ **2.** 2317   **3.** (a) 1.93, 1.178 (b) 3.86, 14.136   **4.** 3.3, 3.9

5. (b) $c = \dfrac{1}{2(n-1)}$

Exercise 2.4

1. (a) $\dfrac{4-\theta^2}{n}$ (b) $\dfrac{3-\theta^2}{n}$ (c) T_2 **2.** T_2 **3.** T_2

Miscellaneous Questions on Chapter 2

1. $a = \dfrac{2}{3k+2}$ **3.** T_1 **4.** (a) 0.52 (c) 0.843   **5.** (a) 0.8 (b) 0.046 (c) 0.6 (d) 0.092

6. $\alpha/24$ **7.** 7.215   **10.** (c)(i) $a = \dfrac{3}{4}$, $b = -\dfrac{1}{4}$ **13.** (b)(i) 24.2 (ii) 600

Exercise 3.1

1. (1.28, 4.22)   **2.** 71.16, 80.44   **3.** 64, 1.22   **4.** 2.997, 3.075   **5.** 43

6. (a) (3.42, 3.48) (b) (3.45, 3.51)   **7.** (2.473, 3.779)   **8.** 90%

9. (a) (964.9, 1001.1) (b) 290

Exercise 3.2

1. (19.17, 22.83)   **2.** 2.40, 7.60   **3.** (1.46, 2.14)   **4.** (−0.48, 2.08)

5. (a) (0.042, 1.038) (b) (−0.240, 1.320)   **6.** 45

Exercise 3.3a

1. 7.56, 0.716; 7.046, 7.474   **2.** (15.19, 16.41); 6.59, 7.21   **3.** (1.741, 1.779)

4. 454.26, 0.23475; (453.46, 455.06)   **5.** 7, 4; (6.345, 7.465); £3.17, £3.73

6. 9.765, 9.985   **7.** (14.84, 15.56)   **8.** (1.073, 1.577)

Exercise 3.3b

1. (2.19, 4.01)   **2.** (0.86, 2.14)   **3.** (−0.409, 0.009)   **4.** (1.572, 1.588), (0.156, 0.186)

5. 132, 4; (131.62, 132.38); (2.38, 3.62)   **6.** (17.69, 18.11); (−0.05, 0.45)

7. (4.81, 6.59)   **8.** 18.02, 19.98

Exercise 3.3c

1. 0.333, 0.383   **2.** 0.478, 0.566   **3.** 0.302, 0.368   **4.** (0.387, 0.447)

5. 0.337, 0.398   **6.** (a) (0.145, 0.255) (b) 385   **7.** (a) 0.059, 0.221 (b) 148, 552

8. (a) 8000 (b) 5500, 14500   **9.** 0.065, 0.0174; (0.031, 0.099)

10. 0.66, 0.048; 0.55, 0.73; 3.09, 3.47   **11.** (0.826, 0.945)

Exercise 3.3d

1. 2.26, 2.78   **2.** 0.561, 0.789   **3.** 0.602, 1.064   **4.** (81.02, 85.64)   **5.** 3.38, 4.42
6. 7.37, 8.83   **7.** 1.59, 2.41   **8.** (5.694, 6.506); (0.0015, 0.0034)

Miscellaneous Questions on Chapter 3

1. $\theta + \dfrac{1}{2}, \dfrac{1}{12}$; 1.9, 0.4; 0.0913; 0.303, 0.417   **2.** (i) (6.42, 8.38) (ii) 62

3. (£85.31, £87.49); (−£0.12, £2.52)   **4.** (a) 11 (b) 1.8, 2.6   **5.** −0.29, 1.09; 2.04
6. 4.96, 5.00   **7.** 0.7, 0.0458; 0.61, 0.79   **8.** (a) 68.95, 72.15 (b) 0.09, 4.61
9. 14.41, 14.99 **10.** 0.38, 0.83 **11.** (0.56, 0.65)   **12.** (a) 1.06 (b)(i) (80.15, 80.45)
13. (6.25, 6.46)   **14.** (a) 0.8 (b) 0.04 (c) (0.73, 0.87)   **15.** (a) 28.09 (b) (68.35, 70.05)
16. (49.95, 50.09)   **17.** (a) (0.73, 1.73)   **18.** (a) (0.176, 1.146)

Exercise 4.1a

1. p-value ≈ 0.0485; $\mu < 2000$ **2.** p-value ≈ 0.0094; $\mu < 800$
3. p-value < 0.00006; $\mu < 133$ **4.** p-value ≈ 0.347; reject claim
5. p-value ≈ 0.0367; accept claim **6.** p-value ≈ 0.001; not by that author
7. p-value ≈ 0.008; $\mu < 1$ **8.** p-value ≈ 0.0027; support the complaint

Exercise 4.1b

1. p-value = 0.031; $\mu_1 > \mu_2$ **2.** p-value = 0.027; $\mu_x > \mu_y$
3. p-value = 0.018; John   **4.** p-value = 0.008; claim is justified
5. p-value = 0.1755; cannot distinguish between the two methods
6. p-value = 0.0418; claim is justified   **7.** p-value = 0.061; claim cannot be justified
8. p-value = 0.043; difference is > 15 cm
9. p-value = 0.075; cannot justify that mean reduced by more than 5 seconds
10. p-value = 0.001; $\mu_B > \mu_A$

Exercise 4.2a

1. p-value = 0.011; observed z = 2.286; mean > 15.2
2. p-value = 0.035; observed $|z|$ = 2.111; (a) $\mu > 52$ (b) significance level too small
to justify rejecting $\mu = 52$

3. p-value = 0.772; observed $|z|$ = 0.290; significance level too small to justify rejecting $\mu = 3$

4. p-value = 0.026; observed $z = -1.94$; complaint is justified

5. Reject $\mu = 49.5$ for any $\alpha \geq 0.04$

6. p-value = 0.019; observed $z = -2.08$; significance level too small to justify rejecting $\mu = 12000$

7. p-value = 0.13; observed $|z|$ = 1.515; significance level too small to justify rejecting $\mu = 10\%$

Exercise 4.2b

1. (a) 0.102　(b) p-value = 0.0485; observed $z = 1.660$; $\mu - \lambda < 10$

2. p-value = 0.078; observed $|z|$ = 1.765; significance level too small to justify rejecting $\mu_x = \mu_y$

3. p-value = 0.033; observed $z = 1.838$; more expensive tyres have longer mean lifetime

4. p-value = 0.22; observed $|z|$ = 1.239; significance level too small to decide if different

5. (a) 1.849　**6.** p-value $\approx$ 0.037; observed $|z|$ = 2.082; second section has higher mean

7. p-value $\approx$ 0.014; observed $z = 2.208$; fluoride beneficial

8. p-value $\approx$ 0.161; observed $z = 0.987$; significance level too small to make a decision

9. (a) p-value $\approx$ 0.048; observed $|z|$ = 1.979; method B quicker on average　(b) 4.8%

10. p-value $\approx$ 0.0014; observed $z = 2.995$; hypothesis is true

Miscellaneous Questions on Chapter 4

1. p-value $\approx$ 0.267; significance level too small to justify rejecting $\mu = 3.75$

2. p-value $\approx$ 0.008; switch to B

3. (a) 95% C.I. is (0.16, 6.04)　(b) p-value = 0.038; $\mu_1 > \mu_2$　**4.** 0.1316

5. p-value $\approx$ 0.0065; conclude type A has higher mean score

6. (b)(i) 0.02　**7.** (a)(i) 2.316　(ii) 0.3030　(b) p-value = 0.201

8. (a) 74.89, 0.1191　(c)(i) 0.001　**9.** (a) 15.6, 4　(b) (14.94, 16.26)　(c)(i) 0.093

11. 0.009; A

Exercise 5.1

1. (a) positive　(b) 3.03, 1.11　(c) 5.8　**2.** 0.95, 0.057, 1.58

3. 61.45, 0.857, 82.9　**4.** 2.9, -500, 0.9　**5.** (a) 57.2　(b) -0.48　(c) 47.6　(d) 9.6

6. $y = 23 - 0.325x$; -4.875　**7.** (a) $y = 38.8 + 12.4x$　(b) 12.4

Exercise 5.2

1. (a) 2.41, 3.65 (b) p-value ≈ 0.004; conclude $y > 5.3$

2. (a) 0.93, 0.97 (b) 0.0019; conclude $y < 1.59$ **3.** 81.6, 84.1

4. (a) -565, -435 (b) Conclude $w < 1$ when $t = 250$

5. (a) 47.06, 48.14 (b) -9.55, -9.65 **6.** -5.00, -4.75

7. (a) 12.14, 12.66 (b) 1.06, 1.94 **8.** (1.592, 1.628); (7.96, 8.14)

Exercise 5.3

1. Set 1

Miscellaneous Questions on Chapter 5

1. (i) 2.96, 3.84 (ii) -0.66, -0.64

2. (i) $40\frac{1}{9}$, $-\frac{3}{10}$ (ii)(a) $(-0.50, -0.10)$ (b) (25.5, 30.7) (iii) smaller standard error

3. (a) 10.005, 0.00115 (b) 9.973, 10.037

  (c) p-value $= 0.0083$; conclude true length < 10.65

4. (ii) $y = 15.38 - 2.32x$ (iii) p-value $= 0.025$; conclude $\beta < -2.2$ (iv) 3.21, 3.39

5. (a)(i) $y = 13.72 + 3.56x$ (ii) 3.47, 3.65 (b) p-value $= 0.049$; conclude true value > 30

6. (i) 73.4 (ii) (2.495, 2.705) (iii) 0.059; cannot reject $\alpha = 6.1$ at the 5% sig. level

7. (a) $a = 1.70$, $b = 0.77$ (b) 0.44, 0.87

8. (a) 140.4, 0.3183 (b)(i) 0.294, 0.343 (ii) 149.67, 150.23 (c) 22.5°C

9. (a) 3.81, 1.27 (b)(i) p-value $= 0.332$; cannot reject $\beta = 1.3$ with significance level

  of 0.05 (ii) p-value $= 0.031$; conclude $\alpha < 4.1$

10. (a)(i) 42.2, 7.229 (ii) 77.91, 78.77 (b) not significant

11. (a) 12.04, 0.206 (b)(i) 0.192, 0.220 (ii) 16.91, 17.47

12. (a)(i) 75, 32.86, 1375, 444.05 (b) (0.072, 0.080)

13. (a) 126.5, -1.025 (b)(i) (8.78, 11.72) (ii) Not significant

14. (a) 40.888, -3.46 (b)(i) $(-4.11, -2.81)$; (4.78, 6.99) (ii) 25.52, 25.32; 0.57, 0.52

15. (a) 15.69, 0.014 (b) Not significant (c) (15.95, 15.98)

16. (a) 27.71 (b) (31.63, 32.29)

17. (a) 18.65 (b) (12.88, 13.92) (c) Conclude $\alpha < 14$

INDEX